Software Engineering Standar

Praxis
Critical
Systems

Software Engineering Standards

C. Mazza
J. Fairclough
B. Melton
D. de Pablo
A. Scheffer
R. Stevens

Prentice Hall

New York   London   Toronto   Sydney   Tokyo   Singapore

First published 1994 by
Prentice Hall Europe
Campus 400, Maylands Avenue
Hemel Hempstead
Hertfordshire, HP2 7EZ
A division of
Simon & Schuster International Group

Printed and bound in Great Britain by
Redwood Books, Trowbridge, Wiltshire

Library of Congress Cataloging-in-Publication Data

Software engineering standards / C. Mazza, J. Fairclough, B. Melton,
  D. de Pablo, A. Scheffer, R. Stevens
        p.   cm.
    Includes index.
    ISBN 0-13-106568-8
      1. Software engineering—Standards.   I. European Space Agency.
  Board for Software Standardisation and Control.
  QA76.758.S64656   1994
  005.1'02184—dc20   93–49619
                                                                   CIP

British Library Cataloguing in Publication Data

A catalogue record for this book is available from
the British Library

ISBN 0-13-106568-8

  7 8 9   99 98 97 96

TABLE OF CONTENTS

PART 2 PROCEDURE STANDARDS   51

PREFACE

This book contains the Software Engineering Stàndards (PSS-05-0) of the European Space Agency (ESA), modified to remove ESA-specific terminology. This generalised version has been produced through ESA's Technology Transfer Programme.

The first version of the ESA standards was issued in 1984, and they are now mandatory for all ESA software. Inputs from users throughout Europe have helped to improve the Standards, culminating in Issue 2, the baseline for this book. These Standards encapsulate the experience of hundreds of software engineers.

These Standards provide a concise definition of how to develop quality software. They are brief and comprehensible, and based upon sound and practical principles. They cover the aspects essential for every project; within these limitations they allow as much choice as possible to the project manager.

The ESA Software Engineering Standards are controlled by the ESA Board for Software Standardisation and Control (BSSC). The board, whose role is to define and promote the use of the Standards, welcome comments and suggestions from users.

European Space Operations Centre
Robert-Bosch Str 5.
D-6100 Darmstadt
Germany

October 1992

Carlo Mazza (BSSC chairman)
Bryan Melton
Daniel de Pablo
Adriaan Scheffer
Richard Stevens
Jon Fairclough.

INTRODUCTION

1 PURPOSE OF THE STANDARDS

This document describes the software engineering standards to be applied for all deliverable software developed either in house or by industry.

Software is defined in these Standards as the programs, procedures, rules and all associated documentation pertaining to the operation of a computerised system. These Standards are concerned with all software aspects of a system, including its interfaces with the computer hardware and with other components of the system. Software may be either a subsystem of a more complex system or it may be an independent system.

2 STRUCTURE OF THE STANDARDS

These Standards are divided into three parts:

Part 1   **Product Standards**, contains standards, recommendations and guidelines concerning the product, i.e. the software to be defined, implemented, operated and maintained.

Part 2   **Procedure Standards**, describes the procedures which are used to manage a software project.

Part 3   **Appendices**, contains summaries, tables, forms and checklists of mandatory practices.

3 CLASSES OF STANDARD PRACTICES

Three categories of standard practices are used in these Standards: mandatory practices, recommended practices and guidelines.

3.1 Mandatory practices

Sentences containing the word 'shall' are mandatory practices. These practices must be followed, without exception, in all software projects. The word 'must' is used in statements that repeat a mandatory practice.

3.2 Recommended practices

Sentences containing the word 'should' are strongly recommended practices. Justification is needed if they are not followed.

3.3 Guideline practices

Sentences containing the word 'may' are guidelines. No justification is required if they are not followed.

4 APPLYING THE STANDARDS

Software projects vary widely in purpose, size, complexity and availability of resources. Software project management **should** define how the Standards are to be applied in the planning documents (see Part 2). Deciding how standards are to be applied in specific projects is often called 'tailoring'.

4.1 Factors in applying the Standards

A number of factors can influence how the Standards are applied, for example the:
- project cost, both in development and operation;
- number of people required to develop, operate and maintain the software;
- number of potential users of the software;
- amount of software that has to be produced;
- criticality of the software, as measured by the consequences of its failure;
- complexity of the software, as measured by the number of interfaces or a similar metric;
- completeness and stability of the user requirements;
- risk values included with the user requirements.

Note that two man years or less is a small project, twenty man years or more is a large project.

Software project management **should** define a life cycle approach and documentation plan that reflects these factors.

Projects which use any commercial software must procure software against stated requirements. Projects are not expected to reproduce design and implementation documentation about commercial software. The maintenance of such software is a responsibility of the supplier.

The procedures for software production may be embedded in the infrastructure of the working environment; once these procedures have been established, repetitive documentation of them is unnecessary. Groups running many projects **should** ensure that their working practices conform to these Standards. Project documentation **should** reference these practices.

Large, complex software projects may need to extend these Standards. Such projects may need to give more detailed consideration to the procedural and life cycle aspects when there are changing requirements or multiple contractors working in parallel.

4.2 Applying the Standards in a system development

Software is frequently part of a larger system. In this situation a number of activities will already have been performed at 'system level' (as part of the system development life cycle) before the life cycle for any software part of the system can commence.

It is a 'systems engineering' function to define the overall requirements for the system to be built, often expressed in a System Requirement Document (often referred to as an SRD, but not to be confused with a Software Requirements Document). From this system requirements document a decomposition into subsystems is often performed with resulting subsystem specifications. Trade-offs are done to partition the system/subsystems into hardware and software, applying criteria specific to the system to be built (e.g. commonality, reliability, criticality etc). Once the need for a software item has been established, its life cycle, as defined in this standard, can begin. Each of the software items identified in the system will have its individual life cycle.

Many of the user requirements may well exist in the system documentation. It is a false economy to assume that system requirements are sufficient input to the development of a software subsystem. To ensure some consistency in the input to a software project, a User Requirements Document (URD) **should** always be produced. The URD **should** be traceable to the system and/or subsystem documentation.

The responsibilities for the production and change control of the URD **should** be agreed between 'system' and 'software' project management, and recorded in the Software Project Management Plan.

4.3 Methods and tools

These standards do not make the use of any particular software engineering method or tool mandatory. The Standards describe the mandatory practices, recommended practices and guidelines for software engineering projects, and allow each project to decide the best way of implementing them.

References to methods and tools appear in these Standards for two reasons. Firstly, terminology from particular methods becomes, with time, part of computing vocabulary. Secondly, examples of possible ways of implementing the Standards are useful.

Part One
Product Standards

CHAPTER 1
THE SOFTWARE LIFE CYCLE

1.1 INTRODUCTION

This chapter defines the overall software life cycle. The individual phases of the life cycle are described in more detail in subsequent chapters.

In these Standards the term 'software development project' is often used. Clearly the development of software also involves computer hardware aspects. Trade-offs between hardware and software are part of designing a computerised system, except when the hardware configuration is predefined, and constrains the software design.

1.2 PHASES, ACTIVITIES AND MILESTONES

The software life cycle starts when a software product is conceived and ends when it is no longer available for use, i.e. it contains the whole of the development, operations and maintenance activities.

The products of a software development project **shall** be delivered in a timely manner and be fit for their purpose. Software development activities **shall** be systematically planned and carried out. A 'life cycle model' structures project activities into 'phases' and defines what activities occur in which phase. Figure 1.1 shows the life cycle model used in these Standards.

A 'life cycle approach' is a combination of the basic phases of the life cycle model. Section 1.3 describes three possible life cycle approaches which cover most situations.

All software projects **shall** have a life cycle approach which includes the basic phases shown in Figure 1.1:
- UR phase - Definition of the user requirements
- SR phase - Definition of the software requirements
- AD phase - Definition of the architectural design
- DD phase - Detailed design and production of the code
- TR phase - Transfer of the software to operations
- OM phase - Operations and maintenance

PHASES / ITEMS	UR USER REQUIREMENTS DEFINITION	UR/R	SR SOFTWARE REQUIREMENTS DEFINITION	SR/R	AD ARCHITECTURAL DESIGN	AD/R	DD DETAILED DESIGN AND PRODUCTION	DD/R	TR TRANSFER	OM OPERATIONS AND MAINTENANCE
MAJOR ACTIVITIES	• determination of operational environment • identification of user requirements		• construction of logical model • identification of software requirements		• construction of physical model • definition of major components		• module design • coding • unit tests • integration tests • system tests		• installation • provisional acceptance tests	• final acceptance tests • operations • maintenance of code and documentation
DELIVERABLE ITEMS arrow implies under change control	User Requirements Document [URD] →		Software Requirements Document [SRD] →		Architectural Design Document [ADD] →		Detailed Design Document [DDD] → [Code] → Software User Manual [SUM] →		Software Transfer Document [STD] →	Project History Document [PHD] →
REVIEWS		technical reviews	walkthroughs inspections	technical reviews	walkthroughs inspections	technical reviews	walkthroughs inspections	technical reviews		
MAJOR MILESTONES		◀ URD approved		◀ SRD approved		◀ ADD approved		◀ code/DDD/SUM approved	◀ STD delivered provisional acceptance	◀ PHD delivered final acceptance

Figure 1.1 *The Software Life Cycle Model*

The first four phases end with a review, denoted by '/R' (e.g. UR/R is the User Requirements Review). These phases must occur whatever the size, the application (e.g. scientific, administrative, real time, batch), the hardware, the operating system or programming language used, or whether the project is carried out by in-house staff or by industry. Each of these factors, however, influences the development approach, and the style and content of the deliverable items.

In Figure 1.1 the heavy black line marks the boundary of the software life cycle. This begins with the delivery of the User Requirements Document (URD) to the developer for review. The UR/R is the first activity of the software life cycle. Following the approval of the URD, three 'development' phases must take place before the software is transferred to the users for operations. The deliverables of each phase must be reviewed and approved before proceeding to the next. After a period of operations, the software is retired. This event marks the end of the software life cycle.

There are six major milestones that mark progress in the software life cycle. These milestones, shown in Figure 1.1 as filled triangles, are the:

- approval of the User Requirements Document (URD);
- approval of the Software Requirements Document (SRD);
- approval of the Architectural Design Document (ADD);
- approval of the Detailed Design Document (DDD), the Software User Manual (SUM), the code, and the statement of readiness for provisional acceptance testing;
- statement of provisional acceptance and the delivery of the Software Transfer Document (STD);
- statement of final acceptance and the delivery of the Project History Document (PHD).

The last milestone does not fall at the end of a phase, but at the end of the warranty period.

These milestones have been selected as the minimum necessary for a workable contractual relationship. They must be present in all projects. In long projects, additional milestones **should** be added to measure the progress of deliverables.

1.2.1   UR phase: user requirements definition

The UR phase is the 'problem definition phase' of a software project. The scope of the system must be defined. The user requirements must be captured. This may be done by interview or survey, or by building prototypes. Specific user requirements must be identified and documented in the User Requirements Document (URD).

The involvement of the developers in this phase varies according to the familiarity of the users with software. Some users can produce a high quality URD, while others may need help from the developers.

The URD must always be produced. The review of the URD is done by the users, the software and hardware engineers and the managers concerned. The approved URD is the input to the SR phase.

Before the completion of the User Requirements Review (UR/R), a Software Project Management Plan outlining the whole project must be produced by the developer. This plan must contain a cost estimate for the project. Detailed plans for the SR phase must also be produced.

1.2.2   SR phase: software requirements definition

The SR phase is the 'analysis' phase of a software project. A vital part of the analysis activity is the construction of a 'model' describing 'what' the software has to do, and not 'how' to do it. Building prototypes to clarify the software requirements may be necessary.

The principal deliverable of this phase is the Software Requirements Document (SRD). The SRD must always be produced for every software project. Implementation terminology **should** be omitted from the SRD. The SRD must be reviewed formally by the users, by the computer hardware and software engineers, and by the managers concerned, during the Software Requirements Review (SR/R).

During the SR phase, the section of the Software Project Management Plan outlining the rest of the project must be updated. The plan must contain an estimate of the total project cost. Detailed plans for the AD phase must also be produced.

1.2.3   AD phase: architectural design

The purpose of the AD phase is to define the structure of the software. The model constructed in the SR phase is the starting point. This model is transformed into the architectural design by allocating functions to software components and defining the control and data flow between them.

This phase may involve several iterations of the design. Technically difficult or critical parts of the design have to be identified. Prototyping of these parts of the software may be necessary to confirm the basic design assumptions. Alternative designs may be proposed, one of which must be selected.

The deliverable item which constitutes the formal output of this phase is the Architectural Design Document (ADD). The ADD must always be produced for every software project. The ADD must be reviewed formally by the computer hardware and software engineers, by the users, and by the management concerned, during the Architectural Design Review (AD/R).

During the AD phase, a Software Project Management Plan outlining the rest of the project must be produced. This plan must contain an estimate of the project cost (10% accuracy is a good target). Detailed plans for the DD phase must also be produced.

1.2.4   DD phase: detailed design and production

The purpose of the DD phase is to detail the design of the software, and to code, document and test it.

The Detailed Design Document (DDD) and the Software User Manual (SUM) are produced concurrently with coding and testing. Initially, the DDD and SUM contain the sections corresponding to the top levels of the system. As the design progresses to lower levels, related subsections are added. At the end of the phase, the documents are completed and, with the code, constitute the deliverable items of this phase.

During this phase, unit, integration and system testing activities are performed according to verification plans established in the SR and AD phases. As well as these tests, there **should** be checks on software quality.

The three deliverable items (Code, DDD, SUM), which have already been the subject of intermediate reviews during the DD phase, must be formally reviewed by the software engineers and the management concerned, during the Detailed Design Review (DD/R). At the end of the review process, the software can be declared ready for provisional acceptance testing.

1.2.5   TR phase: transfer

The purpose of this phase is to establish that the software fulfils the requirements laid down in the URD. This is done by installing the software and conducting acceptance tests.

When the software has been demonstrated to provide the required capabilities, the software can be provisionally accepted and operations started.

The Software Transfer Document (STD) must be produced during the TR phase to document the transfer of the software to the operations team.

1.2.6   OM phase: operations and maintenance

Once the software has entered into operation, it **should** be carefully monitored to confirm that it meets all the requirements defined in the URD. Some of the requirements, for example those for availability, may take a period of time to validate. When the software has passed all the acceptance tests, it can be finally accepted.

The Project History Document (PHD) summarises the significant managerial information accumulated in the course of the project. This document must be issued after final acceptance. It **should** be reissued at the end of the life cycle, with information gathered in the OM phase.

After final acceptance, the software may be modified to correct errors undetected during earlier phases, or because new requirements arise. This is called 'maintenance'.

For the whole period of operation, particular attention **should** be paid to keeping the documentation up-to-date. Information on faults and failures **should** be recorded to provide the raw data for the establishment of software quality metrics for subsequent projects. Tools **should** be used to facilitate the collection and analysis of quality data.

1.3 LIFE CYCLE APPROACHES

The software life cycle model, shown in Figure 1.1, summarises the phases and activities which must occur in any software project. A life cycle approach, based upon this model, **should** be defined, for each project, in the Software Project Management Plan.

This section defines three common approaches. In the diagrams, the phases of Figure 1.1 have been reduced to boxes. Arrows connecting the boxes represent permitted transitions.

1.3.1 The waterfall approach

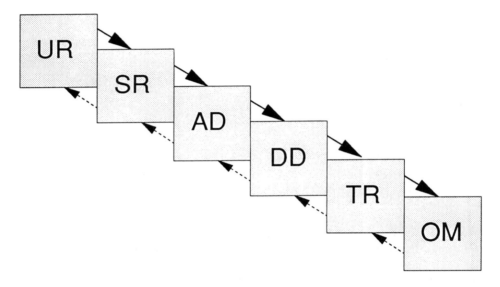

Figure 1.2 *The waterfall approach*

The 'waterfall' approach, shown in Figure 1.2, is the simplest interpretation of the model shown in Figure 1.1. The phases are executed sequentially, as shown by the heavy arrows. Each phase is executed once, although iteration of part of a phase is allowed for error correction, as shown by the dashed arrows. Delivery of the complete system occurs at a single milestone at the end of the TR phase. The approach allows the contractual relationship to be simple.

1.3.2 The incremental delivery approach

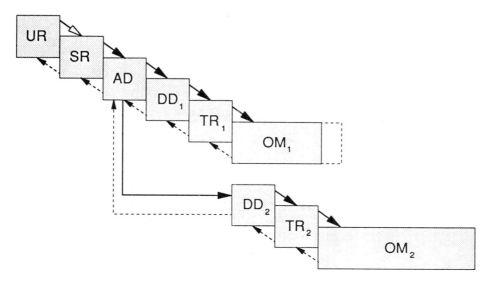

Figure 1.3 *The incremental delivery approach*

The 'incremental delivery' approach, shown in Figure 1.3, is characterised by splitting the DD, TR and OM phases into a number of more manageable units, once the complete architectural design has been defined. The software is delivered in multiple releases, each with increased functionality and capability. This approach is beneficial for large projects, where a single delivery would not be practical. This may occur for a number of reasons such as:

*   certain functions may need to be in place before others can be effective;
*   the size of the development team may necessitate subdivision of the project into a number of deliveries;
*   budgeting considerations may only allow partial funding over a number of years.

In all cases, each deliverable **should** be usable, and provide a subset of the required capabilities.

A disadvantage of the incremental delivery approach is that regression testing is required to confirm that existing capabilities of the software are not impaired by any new release.   The increased amount of testing required increases the cost of the software.

1.3.3   The evolutionary development approach

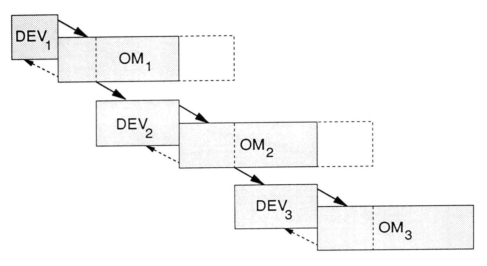

Figure 1.4 *The evolutionary development approach*
The 'DEV' box is equivalent to the UR, SR, AD, DD and TR phases shown in Figure 1.1.

The 'evolutionary' approach, shown in Figure 1.4, is characterised by the planned development of multiple releases. All phases of the life cycle are executed to produce a release. Each release incorporates the experience of earlier releases. The evolutionary approach may be used because, for example:

- some user experience is required to refine and complete the requirements (shown by the dashed line within the OM boxes);
- some parts of the implementation may depend on the availability of future technology;
- some new user requirements are anticipated but not yet known;
- some requirements may be significantly more difficult to meet than others, and it is decided not to allow them to delay a usable delivery.

The dashed extensions to the boxes in Figure 1.4 show that some overlap of OM phases will occur until each new delivery is finally accepted.

In an evolutionary development, the developer **should** recognise the user's priorities and produce the parts of the software that are both important to the user and, possible to develop with minimal technical problems or delays.

The disadvantage of the evolutionary approach is that if the requirements are very incomplete to start with, the initial software structure may not bear the weight of later evolution. Expensive rewrites may be necessary. Even worse, temporary solutions may become embedded in the system and distort its evolution. Further, users may become impatient with the teething troubles of each new release. In each development cycle, it is important to aim for a complete statement of requirements (to reduce risk) and an adaptable design (to ensure later modifiability). In an evolutionary development, all requirements do not need to be fully implemented in each development cycle. However, the architectural design **should** take account of all known requirements.

1.4 PROTOTYPING

The use of prototypes to test customer reaction and design ideas is common to many engineering disciplines. A software prototype implements selected aspects of proposed software so that tests, the most direct kind of verification, can be carried out.

Prototyping is the process of building prototypes. Prototyping within a single phase is a useful means of reducing the risk in a project through practical experience. The output of a prototyping exercise is the knowledge that is gained from implementing or using the prototype software.

The objective of the prototyping activity **should** be clearly stated before the process starts. Prototyping to define requirements is called 'exploratory' prototyping, while that for investigating the feasibility of proposed solutions is called 'experimental' prototyping.

Prototypes usually implement high risk functional, performance or user interface requirements and usually ignore quality, reliability, maintainability and safety requirements. Prototype software is therefore 'pre-operational' and **should** never be delivered as part of an operational system.

1.5 HANDLING REQUIREMENTS CHANGE

The URD and SRD must be 'complete' documents. This means that all known requirements must be included when they are produced. Nevertheless, it is possible that new requirements may arise after the URD and SRD have been approved. Procedures for handling new requirements **should** be established at the beginning of the project.

Design integrity **should** not be compromised when new requirements are incorporated. Such requirements, if accepted by both user and developer, **should be** handled in the same way as the original requirements. The procedure for handling a new user requirement is therefore to:
- generate a new draft of the URD,
- convene a UR review and, if the change is accepted, then
- repeat the SR, AD and DD phases to incorporate the new requirement and its consequences.

A new software requirement is handled in a similar way.

An alternative method for handling new requirements is to institute a Software Review Board after the UR/R instead of after the DD/R. Another method is to use the evolutionary development life cycle approach. However, this merely defers the handling of new requirements to the release following the one that is in preparation, and this may not be sufficient.

The quality of the work done in the UR and SR phases can be measured by the number of requirements that appear in later phases. Especially important is the trend in the occurrence of new requirements. An upward trend is a sure sign that the software is unlikely to be a success.

The availability of software engineering tools may be critical to the success of a project with frequently changing requirements. In projects where requirements are agreed and frozen at the end of the SR phase, the use of paper-based methods for requirements analysis and design specification may be sufficient. In projects where the freezing of requirements is not possible, software engineering tools that allow new requirements and design changes to be assimilated quickly may be essential to avoid serious delays.

CHAPTER 2
THE USER REQUIREMENTS
DEFINITION PHASE

2.1 INTRODUCTION

The UR phase can be called the 'problem definition phase' of the life cycle. The purpose of this phase is to refine an idea about a task to be performed, using computing equipment, into a definition of what is expected from the computer system.

The definition of the user requirements **shall** be the responsibility of the user. The expertise of software engineers, hardware engineers and operations personnel **should** be used to help define and review the user requirements.

An output of the UR phase is the User Requirements Document (URD). This is a critical document for the whole software project because it defines the basis upon which the software is accepted.

The UR phase terminates with formal approval of the URD by the User Requirements Review (UR/R).

2.2 INPUTS TO THE PHASE

No formal inputs are required, although the results of interviews, surveys, studies and prototyping exercises are often helpful in formulating the user requirements.

2.3 ACTIVITIES

The main activity of the UR phase is to capture the user requirements and document them in the URD. The scope of the software has to be established and the interfaces with external systems identified.

Plans of SR phase activities must be drawn up in the UR phase. These plans **should** cover project management, configuration management, verification, validation and quality assurance. These activities are described in more detail in Part 2.

2.3.1 Capture of user requirements

While user requirements originate in the spontaneous perception of needs, user requirements **should** be clarified through the criticism and experience of existing software and prototypes. The widest possible agreement about the user requirements

should be established through interviews and surveys. The knowledge and experience of the potential development organisations **should** be used to advise on implementation feasibility, and, perhaps, to build prototypes. User requirements definition is an iterative process, and requirements capture activities may have to be repeated a number of times before the URD is ready for review.

2.3.2   Determination of operational environment

Determining the operational environment **should** be the first step in defining the user requirements. A clear account **should** be developed of the real world in which the software is to operate. This narrative description may be supported by context diagrams, to summarise the interfaces with external systems (often called 'external interfaces'), and system block diagrams, to show the role of the software in a larger system.

The nature of exchanges with external systems **should** be specified and controlled from the start of the project. The information may reside in an Interface Control Document (ICD), or in the design documentation of the external system. If the external system already exists, then the exchanges may already be defined in some detail, and constrain the design. Alternatively, the definition of the external interfaces may develop throughout the UR, SR and AD phases.

2.3.3   Specification of user requirements

When the operational environment has been established, specific user requirements are extracted and organised. Implementation considerations are omitted, unless they are the essence of the requirement.

2.3.3.1   Classification of user requirements

User requirements fall into two categories:
- capabilities needed by users to solve a problem or achieve an objective;
- constraints placed by users on how the problem is to be solved or the objective achieved.

Capability requirements describe functions and operations needed by users. Quantitative statements that specify performance and accuracy attributes **should** form part of the specification of a capability.

Space and time dimensions can be useful for organising capability requirements. It is often convenient to describe capability requirements in terms of a sequence of operations.

Constraint requirements place restrictions on how software can be built and operated. For example, definitions of external communications, hardware and software interfaces may already exist, either because the software is a part of a larger system, or because the user requires that certain protocols, standards, computers, operating systems, library or kernel software be used.

The Human-Computer Interaction (HCI) requirements will vary according to the type of software under consideration. For interactive systems, the users may wish to provide examples of the dialogue that is required, including the hardware to be used (e.g. keyboard, mouse, colour display etc), and assistance provided by the software (e.g. online help). For batch systems, it may be sufficient to indicate the parameters that need to be varied and the output medium and format required.

Constraints that users may wish to place on the software include the quality attributes of adaptability, availability, portability and security. The user **shall** describe the consequences of losses of availability, or breaches of security, so that developers can fully appreciate the criticality of each function.

The user may choose to make additional standards applicable; such requirements are additional constraints on the development.

2.3.3.2   Attributes of user requirements

Each user requirement must include the attributes listed below.

1. **Identifier** - each user requirement **shall** include an identifier, to facilitate tracing through subsequent phases.

2. **Need** - essential user requirements **shall** be marked as such. Essential user requirements are non-negotiable; others may be less vitally important and subject to negotiation.

3. **Priority** - for incremental delivery, each user requirement **shall** include a measure of priority so that the developer can decide the production schedule.

4. **Stability** - some user requirements may be known to be stable over the expected life of the software; others may be more dependent on feedback from the SR, AD and DD phases, or may be subject to change during the software life cycle. Such unstable requirements **should** be flagged.

5. **Source** - the source of each user requirement **shall** be stated. This may be a reference to an external document (e.g. system requirement document) or the name of the user, or user group, that provided the user requirement.

6. **Clarity** - a user requirement is clear if it has one, and only one, interpretation. Clarity implies lack of ambiguity. If a term used in a particular context has multiple meanings, the term **should** be qualified or replaced with a more specific term.

7. **Verifiability** - each user requirement **shall** be verifiable. This means that it must be possible to:
   • check that the requirement has been incorporated in the design;
   • prove that the software will implement the requirement;
   • test that the software does implement the requirement.

2.3.4 Reviews

The outputs of the UR phase **shall** be formally reviewed during the User Requirements Review (UR/R). This **should** be a technical review (see Part 2, Chapter 4). Participants **should** include the users, operators, developers (hardware and software engineers) and the managers concerned.

User requirements which are rejected in the review process do not have to be removed from the URD, especially if it is anticipated that resources may be available at some later date to implement them. Non-applicable user requirements **shall** be clearly flagged in the URD.

2.4 OUTPUTS FROM THE PHASE

The main outputs of the phase are the URD and the plans for the SR phase.

2.4.1 User Requirements Document

An output of the UR phase **shall** be the User Requirements Document (URD). The URD **shall** always be produced before a software project is started. The recommended table of contents for the URD is provided in Appendix C.

The URD **shall** provide a general description of what the user expects the software to do. All known user requirements **shall** be included in the URD. The URD **should** state the specific user requirements as clearly and consistently as possible.

The URD **shall** describe the operations the user wants to perform with the software system. The URD **shall** define all the constraints that the user wishes to impose upon any solution. The URD **shall** describe the external interfaces to the software system, or reference them in ICDs that exist or are to be written.

Change control of the URD **should** be the responsibility of the user. If a user requirement changes after the URD has been approved, then the user **should** ensure that the URD is changed and resubmitted to the UR/R board for approval.

2.4.2 Acceptance test plans

Acceptance test plans must be defined in the acceptance test section of the Software Verification and Validation Plan (SVVP/AT/Plans, see Part 2, Chapter 4). These plans outline the approach to demonstrating that the software will meet the user requirements.

2.4.3 Project management plan for the SR phase

The outline project plan, the estimate of the total project cost, and the management plan for the SR phase, must be documented in the SR phase section of the Software Project Management Plan (SPMP/SR, see Part 2, Chapter 2).

2.4.4 Configuration management plan for the SR phase

The configuration management procedures for the documents, CASE tool products and prototype software, to be produced in the SR phase, must be documented in the Software Configuration Plan (SCMP/SR, see Part 2, Chapter 3).

2.4.5 Verification and validation plan for the SR phase

The SR phase review and traceability procedures must be documented in the Software Verification and Validation Plan (SVVP/SR, see Part 2, Chapter 4).

2.4.6 Quality assurance plan for the SR phase

The SR phase quality monitoring procedures must be defined in the Software Quality Assurance Plan (SQAP/SR, see Part 2, Chapter 5).

CHAPTER 3
THE SOFTWARE REQUIREMENTS
DEFINITION PHASE

3.1 INTRODUCTION

The SR phase can be called the 'problem analysis phase' of the life cycle. The purpose of this phase is to analyse the statement of user requirements in the URD and produce a set of software requirements as complete, consistent and correct as possible.

The definition of the software requirements is the responsibility of the developer. Participants in this phase **should** include users, software engineers, hardware engineers and operations personnel. They all have a different concept of the end product, and these concepts must be analysed, and then synthesised, into a complete and consistent statement of requirements about which everyone can agree. Project management **should** ensure that all parties are consulted, so that the risk of incompleteness and error is minimised.

An output of this phase is the Software Requirements Document (SRD). As well as defining 'what' the product must do, it is also the reference against which both the design and the product will be verified. Although 'how' aspects may have to be addressed, they **should** be eliminated from the SRD, except those that constrain the software.

The software requirements definition phase terminates with formal approval of the SR phase outputs by the Software Requirements Review (SR/R).

3.2 INPUTS TO THE PHASE

The inputs to the SR phase are the:
- User Requirements Document (URD);
- Software Project Management Plan for the SR phase (SPMP/SR);
- Software Configuration Management Plan for the SR phase (SCMP/SR);
- Software Verification and Validation Plan for the SR phase (SVVP/SR);
- Software Quality Assurance Plan for the SR phase (SQAP/SR).

3.3   ACTIVITIES

SR phase activities **shall** be carried out according to the plans defined in the UR phase. Progress against plans **should** be continuously monitored by project management and documented at regular intervals in progress reports.

The main SR phase activity is to transform the user requirements stated in the URD into the software requirements stated in the SRD. This is achieved by analysing the problem, as stated in the URD, and building a coherent, comprehensive description of what the software is to do. The SRD contains a developer's view of the problem, rather than the user's. This view **should** be based upon a model of the system, built according to a recognised, documented method.

Software requirements may require the construction of prototypes to clarify or verify them. Requirements which cannot be justified by modelling, or whose correctness cannot be demonstrated in a formal way, may need to be prototyped. User interface requirements often need this kind of 'exploratory prototyping'.

Plans of AD phase activities must be drawn up in the SR phase. These plans must cover project management, configuration management, verification, validation and quality assurance. These activities are described in more detail in Part 2.

3.3.1   Construction of the logical model

The developer **shall** construct an implementation-independent model of what is needed by the user. This is called a 'logical model', and it is used to produce the software requirements.

A recognised method for software requirements analysis **shall** be adopted and applied consistently in the SR phase. The logical model may be constructed by top-down decomposition of the main function, as inferred from the URD, into a hierarchy of functions. Modelling is an iterative process. Parts of the model may need to be respecified many times before a complete, coherent and consistent description is achieved.

Walkthroughs, reviews and inspections **should** be used to ensure that the specification of each level has been agreed before proceeding to the next level of detail. A good quality logical model **should** satisfy the rules listed below.

1. Functions **should** have a single definite purpose. Function names **should** have a declarative structure (e.g. 'Validate Telecommands'), and say 'what' is to be done rather than 'how'. Good naming allows design components with strong cohesion to be easily derived (see Part 1, Section 4.3.1.3).
2. Functions **should** be appropriate to the level at which they appear (e.g. 'Calculate Checksum' **should** not appear at the same level as 'Verify Telecommands').
3. Interfaces **should** be minimised. This allows design components with weak coupling to be easily derived (see Part 1, Section 4.3.1.3).
4. Each function **should** be decomposed into no more than seven sub-functions.
5. The model **should** omit implementation information (e.g. file, record, task, module);

6. The performance attributes of each function (capacity, speed etc) **should** be stated;
7. Critical functions **should** be identified.

In all but the smallest projects, CASE tools **should** be used for building a logical model. They make consistent models easier to construct and modify.

3.3.2 Specification of software requirements

The software requirements are obtained by examining the model and classifying them in terms of:

(a) Functional requirements
(b) Performance requirements
(c) Interface requirements
(d) Operational requirements
(e) Resource requirements
(f) Verification requirements
(g) Acceptance testing requirements
(h) Documentation requirements
(i) Security requirements
(j) Portability requirements
(k) Quality requirements
(l) Reliability requirements
(m) Maintainability requirements
(n) Safety requirements

While other classifications of requirements can be conceived, developers **should** use this classification, with the definitions described in Section 3.3.2.1.

Software requirements **should** be rigorously described. Various alternatives to natural language are available and their use is encouraged. Wherever possible, software requirements **should** be stated in quantitative terms to increase their verifiability.

As the requirements are compiled, they must include identifiers, references and measures of need, priority and stability. The requirements must be complete and consistent. Duplication is to be avoided.

3.3.2.1 Classification of software requirements

(a) **Functional requirements.** These specify 'what' the software has to do. They define the purpose of the software. The functional requirements are derived from the logical model, which is in turn derived from the user's capability requirements. In order that they may be stated quantitatively, the functional requirements may include performance attributes.

(b) **Performance requirements.** These specify numerical values for measurable variables (e.g. rate, frequency, capacity, and speed). Performance requirements may be incorporated in the quantitative specification of each function, or stated as separate requirements. Qualitative statements are unacceptable (e.g.

replace 'quick response' with 'response time must be less than x seconds for y% of the cases with an average response time of less than z seconds'). The performance attributes may be presented as a range of values, for example the:
- worst case that is acceptable;
- nominal value, to be used for planning;
- best case value, to indicate where growth potential is needed.

(c) **Interface requirements.** These specify hardware, software or database elements with which the system, or system component, must interact or communicate. Interface requirements **should** be classified into software, hardware and communications interfaces. Software interfaces could include operating systems, software environments, file formats, database management systems and other software applications. Hardware interface requirements may specify the hardware configuration. Communications interface requirements constrain the nature of the interface to other hardware and software. They may demand the use of a particular network protocol, for example. External interface requirements **should** be described, or referenced in ICDs. User interface requirements **should** be specified under 'Operational Requirements' (see below). Interface requirements can be illustrated with system block diagrams (e.g. to show the hardware configuration).

(d) **Operational requirements.** These specify how the system will run and how it will communicate with the human operators. Operational requirements include all user interface, usability and human-computer interaction requirements as well as the logistical and organisational requirements. Examples are: the screen layout, the content of error messages, help systems etc. It is often useful to define the semantics and syntax of commands.

(e) **Resource requirements.** These specify upper limits on physical resources such as processing power, main memory, disc space etc. These are especially needed when extension of processing hardware late in the life cycle becomes too expensive, as in many embedded systems.

(f) **Verification requirements.** These specify the constraints on how the software is to be verified. The verification requirements constrain the SVVP. They might include requirements for simulation, emulation, live tests with simulated inputs, live tests with real inputs, and interfacing with the testing environment.

(g) **Acceptance testing requirements.** These specify the constraints on how the software is to be validated. The acceptance testing requirements constrain the SVVP.

(h) **Documentation requirements.** These specify project-specific requirements for documentation in addition to those contained in these Standards (e.g. the detailed format of the Software User Manual).

(i) **Security requirements.** These specify the requirements for securing the system against threats to confidentiality, integrity and availability. Examples of security requirements are interlocking operator commands, inhibiting of commands, read-only access, password system and computer virus protection. The level of physical protection needed of the computer facilities may also be stated (e.g. backups are to be kept in a fire-proof safe off-site).

(j) **Portability requirements.** These specify the ease of modifying the software to execute on other computers and operating systems. Possible computers and operating systems, other than those of the target system, **should** be stated.

(k) **Quality requirements.** These specify attributes of the software that ensure that it will be fit for its purpose (other than the major quality attributes of reliability, maintainability and safety, which **should** always be specified). Where appropriate, software quality attributes **should** be specified in measurable terms (i.e. with the use of metrics).

(l) **Reliability requirements.** These specify the acceptable mean time interval between failures of the software, averaged over a significant period (MTBF). They may also specify the minimum time between failures that is ever acceptable. Reliability requirements may have to be derived from the user's availability requirements.

(m) **Maintainability requirements.** These specify how easy it is to repair faults and adapt the software to new requirements. The ease of performing these tasks **should** be stated in quantitative terms, such as mean time to repair a fault (MTTR). They may include constraints imposed by the potential maintenance organisation. Maintainability requirements may be derived from the user's availability and adaptability requirements.

(n) **Safety requirements.** These specify any requirements to reduce the possibility of damage that can follow from software failure. Safety requirements may identify critical functions whose failure may be hazardous to people or property.

3.3.2.2   Attributes of software requirements

Each software requirement must include the attributes listed below.

1. **Identifier** - each software requirement **shall** include an identifier, to facilitate tracing through subsequent phases.
2. **Need** - essential software requirements **shall** be marked as such. Essential software requirements are non-negotiable; others may be less vitally important and subject to negotiation.
3. **Priority** - for incremental delivery, each software requirement **shall** include a measure of priority so that the developer can decide the production schedule.
4. **Stability** - some requirements may be known to be stable over the expected life of the software; others may be more dependent on feedback from the design phase, or may be subject to change during the software life cycle. Such unstable requirements **should** be flagged.
5. **Source** - references that trace software requirements back to the URD **shall** accompany each software requirement.

6. **Clarity** - a requirement is clear if it has one, and only one, interpretation. Clarity implies lack of ambiguity. If a term used in a particular context has multiple meanings, the term **should** be qualified or replaced with a more specific term.
7. **Verifiability** - each software requirement **shall** be verifiable. This means that it must be possible to:
   * check that the requirement has been incorporated in the design;
   * prove that the software will implement the requirement;
   * test that the software does implement the requirement.

3.3.2.3   Completeness of software requirements

Completeness has two aspects:
   * no user requirement has been overlooked;
   * an activity has been specified for every possible set of inputs.

For the SRD to be complete, each requirement in the URD must be accounted for. A traceability matrix must be inserted in the SRD to prove completeness.

The phrase 'To Be Defined' (TBD) indicates incompleteness. There must be no TBDs in the SRD.

3.3.2.4   Consistency of software requirements

A set of requirements is consistent if, and only if, no set of individual requirements conflict. There are a number of types of inconsistency, for example:
   * different terms used for the same thing;
   * the same term used for different things;
   * incompatible activities happening at the same time;
   * activities happening in the wrong order.

The achievement of consistency is made easier by using methods and tools.

3.3.2.5   Duplication of software requirements

Duplication of requirements **should** be avoided, although some duplication may be necessary if the SRD is to be understandable. There is always a danger that a requirement that overlaps or duplicates another will be overlooked when the SRD is updated. This leads to inconsistencies. Where duplication occurs, cross-references **should** be inserted to enhance modifiability.

3.3.3   Reviews

The outputs of the SR phase **shall** be formally reviewed during the Software Requirements Review (SR/R). This **should** be a technical review (see Part 2, Chapter 4). Participants **should** include the users, the operations personnel, the developers and the managers concerned.

3.4 OUTPUTS FROM THE PHASE

The main outputs of the phase are the SRD and the plans for the AD phase.

Progress reports, configuration status accounts, and audit reports are also outputs of the phase. These **should** always be archived by the project.

3.4.1 Software Requirements Document

An output of the SR phase **shall** be the Software Requirements Document (SRD).

The SRD **shall** be complete. The SRD **shall** cover all the requirements stated in the URD. A table showing how user requirements correspond to software requirements **shall** be placed in the SRD. This demonstrates forwards traceability and can be used to prove completeness.

The SRD **shall** be consistent. Software engineering methods and tools can help achieve consistency.

The functional requirements **should** be structured top-down in the SRD. Non-functional requirements **should** be attached to functional requirements and therefore can appear at all levels of the hierarchy, and apply to all functional requirements below them (inheritance of family attributes).

The SRD **shall** not include implementation details or terminology, unless it has to be present as a constraint. Descriptions of functions, therefore, **shall** say what the software is to do, and must avoid saying how it is to be done. The SRD **shall** avoid specifying the hardware, unless it is a constraint placed by the user.

The outputs of the analysis method, for example 'data flow diagrams' in the case of Structured Analysis, **should** be included, so as to provide the overview needed to permit an understanding of the specific requirements.

Each software requirement must have an identifier, and include measures of need and priority. Software requirements must reference the URD to facilitate backwards traceability.

The SRD may be written in a natural language. This has the important advantage that it presents no additional barriers between the people of different disciplines who are involved during this phase. On the other hand, natural languages have many properties that are undesirable in specifications (ambiguity, imprecision and inconsistency). Using requirements specification languages can eliminate many of these problems, and these range in rigor from Structured English to Formal Methods such as Z or VDM. Formal methods **should** be considered for the specification of safety-critical systems. If a requirements specification language is used, explanatory text, written in natural language, **should** be included in the SRD to enable it to be reviewed by those not familiar with the specification language.

The SRD **shall** be compiled according to the table of contents provided in Appendix C, which is derived from ANSI/IEEE Std 830-1984, Guide to Software Requirements Specifications.

3.4.2   System test plans

System test plans must be defined in the system test section of the Software Verification and Validation Plan (SVVP/ST/Plans, see Part 2, Chapter 4). These plans outline the approach to demonstrating that the software will meet the software requirements.

3.4.3   Project management plan for the AD phase

The outline project plan, the cost estimate for the complete project, and the management plan for the AD phase, must be documented in the AD phase section of the Software Project Management Plan (SPMP/AD, see Part 2, Chapter 2).

3.4.4   Configuration management plan for the AD phase

The configuration management procedures for the documents, CASE tool products and prototype software, to be produced in the AD phase, must be documented in the Software Configuration Management Plan (SCMP/AD, see Part 2, Chapter 3).

3.4.5   Verification and validation plan for the AD phase

The AD phase review and traceability procedures must be documented in the Software Verification and Validation Plan (SVVP/AD, see Part 2, Chapter 4).

3.4.6   Quality assurance plan for the AD phase

The AD phase quality monitoring procedures must be defined in the Software Quality Assurance Plan (SQAP/AD, see Part 2, Chapter 5).

CHAPTER 4
THE ARCHITECTURAL DESIGN PHASE

4.1 INTRODUCTION

The AD phase can be called the 'solution phase' of the life cycle. The purpose of this phase is to define a collection of software components and their interfaces to establish a framework for developing the software. This is the 'Architectural Design', and it must cover all the requirements in the SRD.

The architectural design definition is the responsibility of the software engineers. Other kinds of engineers may be consulted during this phase, and representatives of users and operations personnel **should** review the architectural design.

An output of this phase is the Architectural Design Document (ADD). This **should** document each component, and its relationship with other components. The ADD is complete when the level of definition of components and interfaces is sufficient to enable individuals or small groups to work independently in the DD phase.

The architectural design phase terminates with formal approval of the AD phase outputs by the Architectural Design Review (AD/R).

4.2 INPUTS TO THE PHASE

The inputs to the AD phase are the:
- Software Requirements Document (SRD);
- Software Project Management Plan for the AD phase (SPMP/AD);
- Software Configuration Management Plan for the AD phase (SCMP/AD);
- Software Verification and Validation Plan for the AD phase (SVVP/AD);
- Software Quality Assurance Plan for the AD phase (SQAP/AD).

4.3 ACTIVITIES

AD phase activities **shall** be carried out according to the plans defined in the SR phase. Progress against plans **should** be continuously monitored by project management and documented at regular intervals in progress reports.

The principal activity of the AD phase is to develop the architectural design of the software and document it in the ADD. This involves:

- constructing the physical model;
- specifying the architectural design;
- selecting a programming language;
- reviewing the design.

A recognised method for software design **shall** be adopted and applied consistently in the AD phase. Where no single method provides all the capabilities required, a project-specific method may be adopted, which **should** be a combination of recognised methods.

Plans for the rest of the development must be drawn up in the AD phase. These plans cover project management, configuration management, verification, validation and quality assurance. These activities are described in more detail in Part 2.

4.3.1 Construction of the physical model

The developer **shall** construct a 'physical model' which describes the design of the software, using implementation terminology. The physical model **should** be derived from the logical model, described in the SRD. In transforming a logical model to a physical model, 'design decisions' are made in which functions are allocated to components and their inputs and outputs defined. Design decisions **should** also satisfy non-functional requirements, design quality criteria and implementation technology considerations. Design decisions **should** be recorded.

Modelling is an iterative process. Each part of the model needs to be specified and respecified until a coherent description of each component is achieved.

In all but the smallest projects, CASE tools **should** be used for building the physical model. They make consistent models easier to construct and modify.

4.3.1.1   Decomposition of the software into components

The software **should** be decomposed into a hierarchy of components according to a partitioning method. Examples of partitioning methods are 'functional decomposition' and 'correspondence with real world objects'. There **should** be distinct levels within the hierarchy, with each component occupying a well-defined place.

The method used to decompose the software into its component parts **shall** permit a top-down approach.   Starting from the top-level component, the software is decomposed into a hierarchy of components. The architectural design **should** specify the upper levels of the hierarchy, typically the top three or four.

Top-down decomposition is vital for controlling complexity because it enforces 'information hiding' by demanding that lower-level components behave as 'black boxes'. Only the function and interfaces of a lower-level component are required for the higher-level design. The information necessary to the internal workings of a lower-level component can remain hidden.

Top-down decomposition also demands that each level of the design be described using terms that have an appropriate degree of 'abstraction' (e.g. the terms 'file', 'record', and 'byte' ought to occur at different levels in the design of a file-handling system). The use of the right degree of abstraction at each level assists information hiding.

The bottom-level components in the ADD **should** be sufficiently independent to allow their detailed design and coding to proceed in parallel to that of other components, with a minimum of interaction between programmers. In multi-tasking systems, the lowest level of the Architectural Design **should** be the task level. At the task level, the timing relationships (i.e. before, after or concurrent) between functions are used to allocate them to tasks.

4.3.1.2 Implementation of non-functional requirements

The SRD contains a number of requirements in the non-functional category. These are:
Performance requirements
Interface requirements
Operational requirements
Resource requirements
Verification requirements
Acceptance testing requirements
Documentation requirements
Security requirements
Portability requirements
Quality requirements
Reliability requirements
Maintainability requirements
Safety requirements
The design of each component **should** be reviewed against each of these requirements. While some non-functional requirements may apply to all components in the system, other non-functional requirements may affect the design of only a few components.

4.3.1.3 Design quality criteria

Designs **should** be adaptable, efficient and understandable. Adaptable designs are easy to modify and maintain. Efficient designs make minimal use of available resources. Designs must be understandable if they are to be built, operated and maintained effectively.

Attainment of these goals is assisted by aiming for simplicity in form and function in every part of the design. There are a number of metrics that can be used for measuring complexity, (e.g. number of interfaces per component), and their use **should** be considered.

Simplicity of function is achieved by maximising the 'cohesion' of individual components (i.e. the degree to which the activities internal to the component are related to one another).

Simplicity of form is achieved by:

* minimising the 'coupling' between components (i.e. the number of distinct items that are passed between components);
* ensuring that the function a component performs is appropriate to its level in the hierarchy;
* matching the software and data structures;
* maximising the number of components that use a given component;
* restricting the number of child components to 7 or less;
* removing duplication between components by making new components.

Designs **should** be 'modular', with minimal coupling between components and maximum cohesion within each component. There is minimal duplication between components in a modular design. Components of a modular design are often described as 'black boxes' because they hide internal information from other components. It is not necessary to know how a black box component works to know what to do with it.

Understandable designs employ terminology in a consistent way and always use the same solution to the same problem. Where teams of designers collaborate to produce a design, understandability can be considerably impaired by permitting unnecessary variety. CASE tools, designs standards and design reviews all help to enforce consistency and uniformity.

4.3.1.4   Trade-off between alternative designs

There is no unique design for any software system. Studies of the different options may be necessary. A number of criteria will be needed to choose the best option. The criteria depend on the type of system. For example, in a real-time situation, performance and response time could be important, whereas in an administrative system stability of the data base might be more important.

Prototyping may be performed to verify assumptions in the design or to evaluate alternative design approaches. This is called 'experimental prototyping'. For example, if a program requires fast access to data stored on disc, then various methods of file access could be coded and measured. Different access methods could alter the design approach quite significantly, and prototyping the access method would become an essential part of the design process.

Only the selected design approach **shall** be reflected in the ADD (and DDD). However, the need for the prototyping, listing of code, trade-off criteria, and reasons for the chosen solution, **should** be documented in the Project History Document.

4.3.2   Specification of the architectural design

The architectural design is the fully documented physical model. This **should** contain diagrams showing, at each level of the architectural design, the data flow and control flow between the components. Block diagrams, showing entities such as tasks and files, may also be used to describe the design. The diagramming techniques used **should** be documented or referenced.

4.3.2.1   Functional definition of the components

The process of architectural design results in a set of components having defined functions and interfaces. The functions of each component will be derived from the SRD. The level of detail in the ADD will show which functional requirements are to be met by each component, but not necessarily how to meet them: this will only be known when the detailed design is complete. Similarly, the interfaces between components will be restricted to a definition of the information to exchange, and not how to exchange it (unless this contributes to the success or failure of the chosen design).

For each component the following information **shall** be defined in the ADD:
- data input;
- functions to be performed;
- data output.

Data inputs and outputs **should** be defined as data structures (see next section).

4.3.2.2   Definition of the data structures

Data structures that interface components **shall** be defined in the ADD. External interfaces may be separately documented in an ICD.

Data structure definitions **shall** include the:
- description of each element (e.g. name, type, dimension);
- relationships between the elements (i.e. the structure);
- range of possible values of each element;
- initial values of each element.

4.3.2.3   Definition of the control flow

The definition of the control flow between components is essential for the understanding of the software's operation. The control flow between the components **shall** be defined in the ADD.

Control flow definitions may describe:
- sequential and parallel operations;
- synchronous and asynchronous behaviour.

4.3.2.4   Definition of the computer resource utilisation

The computer resources (e.g. CPU speed, memory, storage, system software) needed in the development environment and the operational environment **shall** be estimated in the AD phase and defined in the ADD. For many software projects, development environment and operational environment will be the same. Any resource requirements in the SRD will constrain the design.

4.3.3   Selection of programming languages

Programming languages **should** be selected that support top-down decomposition, structured programming and concurrent production and documentation. The programming language and the AD method **should** be compatible.

Non-functional requirements may influence the choice of programming language. For example, portability and maintenance considerations suggest that assembler **should** be selected only for very specific and justifiable reasons. The availability of reliable compilers and effective debuggers constrains the selection of a programming language.

4.3.4   Reviews

The architectural design **should** be reviewed and agreed layer by layer as it is developed during the AD phase. The design of any level invariably affects upper layers: a number of review cycles may be necessary before the design of a level can be finalised. Walkthroughs **should** be used to ensure that the architectural design is understood by all those concerned. Inspections of the design, by qualified software engineers, may be used to eliminate design defects.

The outputs of the AD phase **shall** be formally reviewed during the Architectural Design Review (AD/R). This **should** be a technical review (see Part 2, Chapter 4). Participants **should** include the users, the operations personnel, the hardware engineers, software engineers, and the managers concerned.

After the start of the DD phase, modifications to the architectural design can increase costs substantially. The DD phase **should** not be started if there are still doubts, major open points, or uncertainties in the architectural design.

4.4   OUTPUTS FROM THE PHASE

The main outputs of the phase are the ADD and the plans for the DD phase.

Progress reports, configuration status accounts, software verification reports and audit reports are also outputs of the phase. These **should** always be archived by the project.

4.4.1   Architectural Design Document

The Architectural Design Document (ADD) is the key document that summarises the solution. It is the kernel from which the detailed design grows. The ADD **shall** define the major components of the software and the interfaces between them. The ADD **shall** define or reference all external interfaces. The ADD **shall** be an output from the AD phase.

The ADD **shall** be complete, covering all the software requirements described in the SRD. To demonstrate this, a table cross-referencing software requirements to parts of the architectural design **shall** be placed in the ADD.

The ADD **shall** be consistent. Software engineering methods and tools can help achieve consistency, and their output may be included in the ADD.

The ADD **shall** be sufficiently detailed to allow the project leader to draw up a detailed implementation plan and to control the overall project during the remaining development phases. The ADD **should** be detailed enough to enable the cost of the remaining development to be estimated more accurately than in the SRD (10% accuracy is a good target).

The ADD **shall** be compiled according to the table of contents provided in Appendix C, which is derived from ANSI/IEEE Std 1016-1987, Software Design Descriptions. This table of contents implements the approach described in Section 4.3.2.

4.4.2   Integration test plans

Integration test plans must be defined in the integration test section of the Software Verification and Validation Plan (SVVP/IT/Plans, see Part 2, Chapter 4). These plans outline the approach to demonstrating that the software subsystems conform to the ADD.

4.4.3   Project management plan for the DD phase

The estimate of the total project cost, and the management plan for the DD phase, must be documented in the DD phase section of the Software Project Management Plan (SPMP/DD, see Part 2, Chapter 2). An outline plan for the TR and OM phases must also be included.

4.4.4   Configuration management plan for the DD phase

The configuration management procedures for the documents, deliverable code, CASE tool products and prototype software, to be produced in the DD phase, must be documented in the Software Configuration Management Plan (SCMP/DD, see Part 2, Chapter 3).

4.4.5   Verification and validation plan for the DD phase

The DD phase review and traceability procedures must be documented in the Software Verification and Validation Plan (SVVP/DD, see Part 2, Chapter 4).

4.4.6   Quality assurance plan for the DD phase

The DD phase quality monitoring procedures must be defined in the Software Quality Assurance Plan (SQAP/DD, see Part 2, Chapter 5).

CHAPTER 5
THE DETAILED DESIGN AND
PRODUCTION PHASE

5.1 INTRODUCTION

The DD phase can be called the 'implementation phase' of the life cycle. The purpose of the DD phase is to detail the design outlined in the ADD, and to code, document and test it.

The detailed design and production is the responsibility of the software engineers. Other kinds of engineers may be consulted during this phase, and representatives of users and operations personnel may observe system tests. The software may be independently verified by engineers not responsible for detailed design and coding.

Important considerations before starting code production are the adequacy and availability of computer resources for software development. There is no point in starting coding and testing if the computer, operating system and system software are not available or sufficiently reliable and stable. Productivity can drop dramatically if these resources are not adequate. Failure to invest in software tools and development hardware often leads to bigger development costs.

The principal output of this phase are the code, the Detailed Design Document (DDD) and Software User Manual (SUM). The DD phase terminates with formal approval of the code, DDD and SUM by the Detailed Design Review (DD/R).

5.2 INPUTS TO THE PHASE

The inputs to the DD phase are the:
- Architectural Design Document (ADD);
- Integration test plans (SVVP/IT/Plans);
- System test plans (SVVP/ST/Plans);
- Software Project Management Plan for the DD phase (SPMP/DD);
- Software Configuration Management Plan for the DD phase (SCMP/DD);
- Software Verification and Validation Plan for the DD phase (SVVP/DD);
- Software Quality Assurance Plan for the DD phase (SQAP/DD).

5.3   ACTIVITIES

DD phase activities **shall** be carried out according to the plans defined in the AD phase. Progress against plans **should** be continuously monitored by project management and documented at regular intervals in progress reports.

The detailed design and production of software **shall** be based on the following three principles:

- top-down decomposition;
- structured programming;
- concurrent production and documentation.

These principles are reflected in both the software design and the organisation of the work. They help ensure that the software is delivered on time and within budget, because emphasis is placed on 'getting it right first time'. They also have a positive effect on the quality of the software, its reliability, maintainability and safety.

Top-down decomposition is vital for controlling complexity because it enforces 'information hiding' by demanding that lower-level components behave as 'black boxes'. Only the function and interfaces of a lower-level component are required for the higher-level design. The information necessary to the internal workings of a lower-level component can remain hidden.

Structured programming aims to avoid making errors when a module is designed and when code is written. Stepwise refinement of a design into code, composed of the basic sequence, selection and iteration constructs is the main feature of the technique. By reducing the number of coding errors, structured programming dramatically reduces time spent in testing and correcting software. Structured programming also makes code more understandable, reducing time spent in inspection and in maintenance.

Concurrent production and documentation of code is a side effect of stepwise refinement. Design information **should** be retained as commentary in the source code.

5.3.1   Detailed design

In detailed design, lower-level components of the architectural design are decomposed until they can be expressed as modules in the selected programming language. A module is a program unit that is discrete and identifiable with respect to compiling, combining with other units, and loading.

Starting from the bottom-level components in the ADD, the design proceeds to lower levels via stepwise refinement of each module specification.

The guidelines for stepwise refinement are:

- start from functional and interface specifications;
- concentrate on the control flow;
- defer data declarations until the coding phase;
- keep steps of refinement small so that verification is easier;
- review each step as it is made.

The review of each module may be by walkthrough or inspection. The review of a module is complete when it is approved for coding.

The methods and CASE tools used for architectural design **should** be used in the DD phase for the detailed design work.

Although design **should** normally proceed downwards, some of the lowest level components may need to be designed (and coded) first. Examples are device drivers and utility libraries.

5.3.2   Production

5.3.2.1   Coding

When the design of each module is completed, reviewed and approved, it can be coded.

Coding conventions **should** be established and documented in the DDD. They **should** provide rules for:
- presentation, (e.g. header information and comment layout);
- naming programs, subprograms, files, variables and data;
- limiting the size of modules;
- using library routines, especially:
  - operating system routines;
  - commercial library routines (e.g. numerical analysis);
  - project specific utility routines;
- defining constants;
- using compiler specific features not in the language standard;
- error handling.

The standard header (see Part 2, Chapter 3) **should** be made available so that it can be edited, completed and then inserted at the head of each module.

Code **should** be consistent, as this reduces complexity. Rigorous adherence to coding conventions is fundamental to ensuring consistency. Further, consistency is enhanced by adopting the same solutions to the same problems. To preserve code consistency, changes and modifications **should** follow the style of the original code, assuming it was produced to recognised standards.

Code **should** be structured, as this reduces errors and enhances maintainability. Generally, this means resolving it into the basic sequence, selection (i.e. condition) and iteration (i.e. loop) constructs. Practically, the ideas of structured programming require that:
- each module **should** have a single entry and exit point;
- control flow **should** proceed from the beginning to the end;
- related code **should** be blocked together rather than dispersed around the module;
- branching out of a module **should** only be performed under prescribed conditions (e.g. error exit).

Production of consistent, structured code is made easier by using tools such as language-sensitive editors, customised to suit the project conventions.

The coding process includes compilation; not only does this produce the object code needed for testing the run-time behaviour of a module, it is the first step in verifying the code. Compilation normally produces statistics that can be used for the static analysis of the module.

Supplementary code included to assist the testing process **should** be readily identifiable and easy to disable, or remove, after successful testing. Care **should** be taken to ensure that such code does not obscure the module logic.

As the coding of a module proceeds, documentation of the design assumptions, function, structure, interface, internal data and resource utilisation **should** proceed concurrently. This information **should** be recorded in Part 2 of the DDD. The inclusion of this information in the source code is recommended. To avoid the maintenance problem of having the same information in two places, tools to select information required for the DDD from the source code are desirable.

When a module has been documented and successfully compiled, unit testing can begin.

5.3.2.2 Integration

Integration is the process of building a software system by combining components into a working entity.

Integration of components **should** proceed in an orderly function-by-function sequence. This allows the software's operational capabilities to be demonstrated early, increasing management confidence that the project is progressing satisfactorily.

The integration process **shall** be controlled by the software configuration management procedures defined in the SCMP. Good SCM procedures are essential for correct integration.

The top-down approach to integration is to use stubs to represent lower-level modules. As modules are completed and tested, they replace the stubs. In many projects, the need to make shared components available at an early stage forces the integration to be organised initially on a bottom-up, and later on a top-down, basis. Whatever approach to integration is taken, it **should** minimise the time spent in testing, while ensuring that all source statements are verified.

5.3.2.3 Testing

Procedures for developing and documenting the test approach are described in Part 2, Chapter 4.

5.3.2.3.1 Unit testing

Unit tests verify the design and implementation of all components from the lowest level defined in the detailed design up to the lowest level defined in the architectural design (normally the task level). Modules that do not call other modules exist at the lowest level of the detailed design.

Unit tests verify that not only is a module doing what it is supposed to do ('black box' testing), but also that it is doing it in the way it was intended ('white box' testing). The most probable paths through a module **should** be identified and tests designed to ensure these paths are executed. In addition, before a module can be accepted, every statement **shall** be successfully executed at least once. Coverage analysers and symbolic debuggers can be very useful in observing the internal behaviour of a module. For larger systems, tools can ensure that modules are tested systematically.

Unit testing is normally carried out by the individuals or teams responsible for the components' production.

Unit test plans, test designs, test cases, test procedures and test reports are documented in the Unit Test section of the Software Verification and Validation Plan (SVVP/UT).

5.3.2.3.2   Integration testing

Integration testing is also done in the DD phase when the major components are assembled to build the system. These major components are identified in the ADD. Integration tests **should** be directed at verifying that major components interface correctly. Integration testing **should** precede system testing and follow unit testing.

Integration testing **shall** check that all the data exchanged across an interface agree with the data structure specifications in the ADD. Integration testing **shall** confirm that the control flows defined in the ADD have been implemented.

Integration test designs, test cases, test procedures and test reports are documented in the Integration Test section of the Software Verification and Validation Plan (SVVP/IT).

5.3.2.3.3   System testing

System testing is the process of testing an integrated software system. This testing can be done in the development or target environment, or a combination of the two. System testing **shall** verify compliance with system objectives, as stated in the SRD. System testing **should** include such activities as:
- passing data into the system, correctly processing and outputting it (i.e. end-to-end system tests);
- practice for acceptance tests (i.e. verification that user requirements will be met);
- stress tests (i.e. measurement of performance limits);
- preliminary estimation of reliability and maintainability;
- verification of the Software User Manual.

Trends in the occurrence of defects **should** be monitored in system tests; the behaviour of such trends is important for the estimation of potential acceptability.

For most embedded systems, as well as systems using special peripherals, it is often useful or necessary to build simulators for the hardware with which the deliverable system will interface. Such simulators are often required because of:
- late availability of the final system hardware;

- low available test time with the final system hardware;
- desire to avoid damaging delicate and/or expensive hardware.

Simulators are normally a separate project in themselves. Effort **should** be made to ensure that they are available in time, and that they are certified as identical, from an interface point of view, with the target hardware.

System test designs, test cases, test procedures and test reports are documented in the System Test section of the Software Verification and Validation Plan (SVVP/ST).

5.3.3 Reviews

The detailed design **should** be reviewed and agreed layer by layer as it is developed during the DD phase. The design of any level invariably affects upper layers and a number of review cycles may be necessary before the design of a level can be finalised. Walkthroughs **should** be used to ensure that the detailed design is understood by all concerned. Inspections of the design, by qualified software engineers, **should** be used to reduce the occurrence of design defects.

When the detailed design of a major component is finished, a critical design review **shall** be convened to certify its readiness for implementation. The project leader **should** participate in these reviews, together with the team leader and team members concerned.

After modules have been coded and successfully compiled, walkthroughs or inspections **should** be held to verify that the implementation conforms to the design.

After production, the DD Review (DD/R) **shall** consider the reports of the verification activities and decide whether to transfer the software. This **should** be a technical review (see Part 2, Chapter 4). Review participants **should** include engineers, user representatives and managers.

5.4 OUTPUTS FROM THE PHASE

The main outputs of the phase are the code, DDD, SUM and the plans for the TR phase.

Progress reports, configuration status accounts, software verification reports and audit reports are also outputs of the phase. These **should** always be archived by the project.

5.4.1 Code

The developer **should** deliver all the items needed to execute and modify any part of the software produced in the project, e.g:

- source files;
- command procedure files;
- configuration management tools;
- source files for test software;
- test data;
- build and installation procedures.

All deliverable code **shall** be identified in a configuration item list.

5.4.2 Detailed Design Document

The DDD grows as the design proceeds to the lowest level of decomposition. Documentation **should** be produced concurrently with detailed design, coding and testing. In large projects, it may be convenient to organise the overall DDD into several volumes. The DDD **shall** be an output of the DD phase. A recommended table of contents of the DDD is provided in Appendix C.

Part 1 of the DDD defines design and coding standards and tools, and **should** be prepared as the first activity of the DD phase, before work starts on detailed design and coding.

Part 2 of the DDD expands as the design develops. Part 2 of the DDD **shall** have the same structure and identification scheme as the code itself, with a 1:1 correspondence between sections of the documentation and the software components.

The DDD **shall** be complete, accounting for all the software requirements in the SRD. A table cross-referencing software requirements to the detailed design components **shall** be placed in the DDD.

5.4.3 Software User Manual

A Software User Manual (SUM) **shall** be an output of the DD phase. The recommended table of contents for a SUM is provided in Appendix C. The rules for the style and content of the Software User Manual are based on ANSI/IEEE Std 1063-1987, 'Software User Documentation'. Two styles of user documentation are useful: the 'instruction', or 'tutorial', style and the 'reference' style. While the instruction style is oriented towards helping new users, the reference style is more suited to more experienced users who need information about specific topics.

In the instruction section of the SUM, material is ordered according to the learning path, with the simplest, most necessary operations appearing first and more advanced, complicated operations appearing later. The size of this section depends on the intended readership; some users may understand the software after a few examples (and can switch to using the reference section) whilst other users may require many worked examples.

The reference section of the SUM presents the basic operations, ordered for easy reference (e.g. alphabetically). Reference documentation **should** be more formal, rigorous and exhaustive than the instructional section. For example a command may be described in the instruction section in concrete terms, with a specific worked example. The description in the reference section **should** describe all the parameters, qualifiers and keywords, with several examples.

The development of the SUM **should** start as early as possible. Establishing the potential readership for the SUM **should** be the first step. This information is critical for establishing the style of the document. Useful information may be found in the section 'User Characteristics' in the URD.

The Software User Manual may be large, spread over several volumes. The SUM may be made available electronically, for example as part of an online help facility. There **should** be specific software requirements for such facilities.

5.4.4   Project management plan for the TR phase

The management plan for the TR phase must be documented in the DD phase section of the Software Project Management Plan (SPMP/TR, see Part 2, Chapter 2). This plan may also cover the period up to final acceptance.

5.4.5   Configuration management plan for the TR phase

The TR phase procedures for the configuration management of the deliverables, in the operational environment, must be documented in the Software Configuration Management Plan (SCMP/TR, see Part 2, Chapter 3).

5.4.6   Acceptance test specification

Acceptance test designs, test cases and test procedures must be documented in the Software Verification and Validation Plan (SVVP/AT, see Part 2, Chapter 4).

5.4.7   Quality assurance plan for the TR phase

The TR phase quality monitoring procedures must be defined in the TR phase section of the Software Quality Assurance Plan (SQAP/TR, see Part 2, Chapter 5).

CHAPTER 6
THE TRANSFER PHASE

6.1 INTRODUCTION

The TR phase can be called the 'handover phase' of the life cycle. The purpose of the TR phase is to install the software in the operational environment and demonstrate to the initiator and users that the software has all the capabilities described in the User Requirements Document (URD).

Installation and checkout of the software is the responsibility of the developer. Representatives of users and operations personnel **shall** participate in acceptance tests. The Software Review Board (SRB) **shall** review the software's performance in the acceptance tests and recommend, to the initiator, whether the software can be provisionally accepted or not.

The principal output of this phase is the Software Transfer Document (STD), which documents the acceptance testing activities.

The TR phase terminates with provisional acceptance of the software and the start of operations.

6.2 INPUTS TO THE PHASE

The inputs to the TR phase are the:
- code;
- Detailed Design Document (DDD);
- Software User Manual (SUM);
- Acceptance Test specification (SVVP/AT).
- Software Project Management Plan for the TR phase (SPMP/TR);
- Software Configuration Management Plan for the TR phase (SCMP/TR);
- Software Quality Assurance Plan for the TR phase (SQAP/TR).

6.3 ACTIVITIES

TR phase activities **shall** be carried out according to the plans defined in the DD phase.

6.3.1 Installation

The first activity of the TR phase is installation of the software. This is done by:
- checking the deliverables against the configuration item list;
- building a system executable in the target environment.

Procedures for building software may vary, depending on the type of software, but the capability of building the system from the components that are directly modifiable by the maintenance team **shall** be established. Maintenance staff **should** exercise the procedures for modifying the software, especially if any unfamiliar software development tools have been supplied.

6.3.2 Acceptance tests

Acceptance tests validate the software, i.e. they demonstrate the capabilities of the software in its operational environment. Acceptance tests **should** be based on the user requirements, as stated in the URD. Acceptance tests plans, test designs, test cases and test procedures are defined in the SVVP. Acceptance tests are executed in the TR phase and the results recorded in the SVVP. A summary of the acceptance test reports **should** be inserted in the STD.

6.3.3 Provisional acceptance

Acceptance tests necessary for provisional acceptance **shall** be indicated in the SVVP. The criterion for provisional acceptance is whether the software is ready for operational use. A period of operations is usually required to show that the software meets all the requirements in the URD.

The provisional acceptance decision **should** be made by the initiator after consultations with the SRB, end-user representatives and operations staff.

6.4 OUTPUTS FROM THE PHASE

6.4.1 Statement of provisional acceptance

The statement of provisional acceptance **shall** be produced by the initiator, on behalf of the users, and sent to the developer. Provisional acceptance marks the end of the TR phase.

6.4.2 Provisionally accepted software system

The provisionally accepted software system **shall** consist of the outputs of all previous phases and modifications found necessary in the TR phase.

6.4.3   Software Transfer Document

The purpose of the Software Transfer Document (STD) is to identify the software that is being transferred and how to build and install it. An output of the TR phase **shall be** the STD. The STD **shall** be handed over from the developer to the maintenance organisation at provisional acceptance. The recommended table of contents for the STD is presented in Appendix C.

The STD **shall** contain a summary of the acceptance test reports and all document-ation about software changes performed during the TR phase.

CHAPTER 7
THE OPERATIONS AND
MAINTENANCE PHASE

7.1 INTRODUCTION

In the OM phase, the software first enters practical use. The operation of software is beyond the scope of these Standards, so this chapter only discusses maintenance.

The purpose of software maintenance is to ensure that the product continues to meet the real needs of the end-user. The available resources for maintenance **should** reflect the importance of the product.

Unlike hardware maintenance, which aims to return a hardware product to its original state, software maintenance always results in a change to a software product. Software maintenance staff **should** thoroughly understand the software which they have to alter. Training may be necessary.

The principal output of this phase is the Project History Document (PHD), which summarises the development, operations and maintenance of the product.

7.2 INPUTS TO THE PHASE

The inputs to the OM phase are the:
- statement of provisional acceptance;
- provisionally accepted software system;
- Software Transfer Document.

7.3 ACTIVITIES

Until final acceptance, OM phase activities that involve the developer **shall** be carried out according to the plans defined in the SPMP/TR.

The maintenance organisation may choose to adopt the Software Configuration Management Plan used in the development phases. Alternatively they may choose to produce a new one, specific to their needs. The effort to convert from one configuration management system to another **should** not be underestimated, nor the risks involved ignored (e.g. the loss of configuration items or the incorrect attachment of labels).

The Software Project Management Plans and Software Quality Assurance Plans continue to apply to the activities of development staff, but not to operations and maintenance staff, who **should** develop their own plans.

7.3.1   Final Acceptance

The early part of the OM phase **should** include a warranty period in which the developer **should** retain responsibility for correcting errors. The end of the warranty period is marked by final acceptance.

The criterion for final acceptance is whether the software meets all requirements stated in the URD. All the acceptance tests **shall** have been successfully completed before the software is finally accepted.

The final acceptance decision **should** be made by the initiator after consultations with the SRB, end-user representatives and operational staff. Even when no contractor is involved, there **shall** be a final acceptance milestone to arrange the formal handover from software development to maintenance.

Whenever the handover is performed, the last document formally released by the engineering (as opposed to maintenance) project leader, must be the first issue of the Project History Document (PHD).

7.3.2   Maintenance

After this warranty period, maintenance of the software may be transferred from the developer to a dedicated maintenance organisation. A maintenance organisation **shall** be designated for every software product in operational use. Resources **shall** be assigned to a product's maintenance until it is retired.

Maintenance of software **should** be driven by the occurrence of problems and new requirements. The SRB controls problem handling activity, and **shall** authorise all modifications. Responsibility for minor modifications and emergency changes may be delegated to maintenance staff, depending on the level of criticality.

Procedures for software modification **shall** be defined. This is normally done by carrying over the configuration management and verification procedures from the development phase. Consistency between code and documentation **shall** be maintained.

Some software problems can give rise to new requirements. A user, after experience with the software, may propose a modification (in an SPR). The SRB, classifying the problem as a new or changed requirement, drafts changes to the URD and reviews it with the users concerned. Users may also draft changes to the URD and put them forward to the SRB.

New requirements may also arise because the original requirements defined in the UR and SR phases were not appropriate, or because the user's needs change. The maintenance budget **should** support a realistic level of requirement-change activity. Major new requirements **should** be handled as a separate software development project, and be separately budgeted.

Users **should** be kept informed of problems. If possible, software items which are the subject of problem reports **should** be withdrawn from use while the problem is corrected. When withdrawal is not possible, temporary work-around solutions are permitted, provided the safety of the system is not impaired. All software modifications must be documented, even temporary ones.

When software is changed, regression tests **should** be performed to ensure that the change has not caused new faults. Regression test cases may be a subset of the acceptance test cases.

7.4 OUTPUTS FROM THE PHASE

7.4.1 Statement of final acceptance

The statement of final acceptance **shall** be produced by the initiator, on behalf of the users, and sent to the developer. Its delivery marks the formal handover of the software. The precondition of final acceptance is that all the acceptance tests have been executed satisfactorily.

7.4.2 Project History Document

The Project History document (PHD) **should** be produced by the software project manager. It summarises the main events and outcome of the project. The PHD is useful to future projects for:
- estimating the effort required;
- setting up the organisation;
- finding successful methods;
- advising about problems and pitfalls.

The PHD is the place where estimates, made in the planning stages, are compared with actual events. The accuracy of predictions of the project schedule, software volume, manpower requirements, hardware requirements and cost **should** be measured. Productivity **should** be estimated using the measurements of software volume, resources and time.

Preparation of the PHD forces a project manager to consider progress carefully, and to draw personal and organisational conclusions when the events concerned are fresh in the project manager's mind. Accordingly, the project manager **should** start making notes for the PHD at the beginning of the project. At the end of each phase, the plans made for the previous phase **should** be compared with what actually happened. This knowledge can also help in planning the next phase.

The PHD **shall** be delivered to the initiator after final acceptance, who **should** make it available to the maintenance organisation. The chapter describing the performance of the system **should** be added by the designated maintenance organisation during the OM phase and updated when the product is retired. The recommended table of contents for the PHD is presented in Appendix C.

7.4.3   Finally accepted software system

This consists of one or more sets of documentation, source, object and executable code corresponding to the current versions and releases of the product.

Part Two
Procedure Standards

CHAPTER 1
MANAGEMENT OF THE
SOFTWARE LIFE CYCLE

1.1 INTRODUCTION

Part 2 of these Standards describes the activities that are essential for managing the software life cycle. Whereas Part 1 describes the activities and products of each phase of the life cycle, Part 2 discusses management activities which are performed throughout all development phases.

The goal of the management activities is to build the product within budget, according to schedule, with the required quality. To achieve this, plans must be established for:

- software project management;
- software configuration management;
- software verification and validation;
- software quality assurance.

Figure 1.1 summarises how these plans must be documented. Plans for project management, configuration management, verification, validation and quality assurance are split into sections. Each section plans the activities for subsequent phases. While the same structure may be repeated in each section of a document, the actual contents may vary. Titles of documents are separated from their section names by '/' (e.g. SPMP/SR is the SR phase section of the Software Project Management Plan).

Figure 1.1 does not include the plans required to manage the maintenance of the software in the period between final acceptance and retirement. The maintenance organisation may choose to reuse development plans or produce new plans.

ACTIVITY / PLAN	USER REQUIREMENTS REVIEW		SOFTWARE REQUIREMENTS DEFINITION		ARCHITECTURAL DESIGN		DETAILED DESIGN AND PRODUCTION	
	Activity	Output	Activity	Output	Activity	Output	Activity	Output
SOFTWARE PROJECT MANAGEMENT	Estimate project cost Plan SR phase WBS & staffing Outline plan for whole project	SPMP/SR	Estimate project cost to 30% accuracy Plan AD phase WBS & staffing	SPMP/AD	Estimate project cost to 10% accuracy Plan DD phase WBS & Staffing	SPMP/DD	Detail DD phase WBS Plan TR phase WBS & Staffing	SPMP/DD updates SPMP/TR
SOFTWARE CONFIGURATION MANAGEMENT	Define SR phase procedures for: - documents - CASE tool products - prototype code	SCMP/SR	Define AD phase procedures for: - documents - CASE tool products - prototype code	SCMP/AD	Define DD phase procedures for: - documents - CASE tool products - deliverable code	SCMP/DD	Define operational environment procedures for: - documents - deliverable code	SCMP/TR
SOFTWARE VERIFICATION AND VALIDATION	Define SR phase review and traceability procedures Plan acceptance tests	SVVP/SR SVVP/AT	Define AD phase review and traceability procedures Plan system tests	SVVP/AD SVVP/ST	Define DD phase review and traceability procedures Plan integration tests	SVVP/DD SVVP/IT	Define acceptance tests Define system tests Define integration tests Plan and define unit tests	SVVP/AT updates SVVP/ST updates SVVP/IT updates SVVP/UT
SOFTWARE QUALITY ASSURANCE	Plan SR phase monitoring activities Outline plan for whole project	SQAP/SR	Plan AD phase monitoring activities	SQAP/AD	Plan DD phase monitoring activities	SQAP/DD	Plan TR phase monitoring activities	SQAP/TR

Figure 1.1 Software Management Plans

1.2 SOFTWARE PROJECT MANAGEMENT

A project manager, or project management team, has to plan, organise, staff, monitor, control and lead a software project. The project manager is responsible for writing the Software Project Management Plan (SPMP). The project manager leads the development team and is the principal point of contact between them and the initiator, end-users and other parties.

1.3 SOFTWARE CONFIGURATION MANAGEMENT

Proper configuration management is essential for control of a software product. A component may function perfectly well, but either a fault in integration or a mistake in identification can result in obscure errors. This standard defines requirements for identifying, controlling, releasing and changing software items and recording their status. Procedures for managing the software configuration must be defined in the Software Configuration Management Plan (SCMP).

1.4 SOFTWARE VERIFICATION AND VALIDATION

These standards adopt a general definition of verification as the process of reviewing, inspecting, testing, checking and auditing software products. Verification is essential to assure that the product will be fit for its purpose. The verification approach **should** be planned by project management and carried out by development staff.

In these Standards, 'validation' is the evaluation of software at the end of the development process to ensure compliance with user requirements. Validation is done in the TR phase.

All verification and validation activities must be documented in the Software Verification and Validation Plan (SVVP).

1.5 SOFTWARE QUALITY ASSURANCE

The quality assurance activity is the process of verifying that these Standards are being applied. In small projects this is done by the project manager, but in large projects specific staff **should** be allocated to the role. The Software Quality Assurance Plan is the document which describes how adherence to the Standards is to be verified.

CHAPTER 2
SOFTWARE PROJECT MANAGEMENT

2.1 INTRODUCTION

Software Project Management (SPM) is 'the process of planning, organising, staffing, monitoring, controlling and leading a software project' (ANSI/IEEE Std 1058.1-1987). The Software Project Management Plan (SPMP) is the controlling document for managing a software project. The SPMP defines the technical and managerial project functions, activities and tasks necessary to satisfy the requirements of a software project.

The SPMP is updated and refined, throughout the life cycle, as more accurate estimates of the effort involved become possible, and whenever changes in requirements or design occur. A number of methods and tools are available for software project planning and their use is recommended.

During all the phases of the life cycle, project management **should** review how a plan works out in practice. Important deviations between estimates and actuals have to be explained and documented in the Project History Document (PHD), which is issued in the OM phase.

2.2 ACTIVITIES

2.2.1 Organising the project

A key responsibility of software project management is organising all project activities. There are several possible models for the organisation of a software project (e.g. functional and matrix).

Once tasks have been defined, project management must define the team structure to carry them out. Positions in that structure **should** be adequately defined so that each team member has clear responsibilities and lines of authority. These responsibilities **should** be documented in terms of reference and work package descriptions.

2.2.2 Leading the project

Project management decide the objectives and priorities at each stage. They **should** document the assumptions, dependencies and constraints that influence their decisions in the SPMP.

2.2.3 Risk management

Risks threaten a project's success. Project management **should** identify the risks to a project and assess the threat they pose. This is called 'risk analysis'. Examples of potential risk areas are:

- quality and stability of user requirements;
- level of definition and stability of external interfaces;
- adequacy and availability of resources;
- availability and quality of tools;
- staff training and experience;
- definition of responsibilities;
- short time scales;
- technical novelty of the project.

Risks may be quantified by combining the probability of an event with the cost to the project if it does happen. The total risk to the project is the sum of all risks. Probabilities can be estimated from historical data (e.g. sickness rates of employees) or manufacturer's data (e.g. the mean time between failure of a disk drive).

Project management **should** devise a plan for reducing risk levels and ensure that it is carried out. Achievements **should** be measured and the risks reevaluated throughout the project.

Decisions about priorities **should** be supported by risk analysis. Accurate assessment of the impact of decisions relies on quantitative estimation of the factors that **should** change when action is taken.

2.2.4 Technical management

There are many methods and tools that can be applied throughout the software life cycle, which can greatly enhance the quality of the end product and their use is strongly recommended. Project management is responsible for selecting methods and tools, and for enforcing their use.

Technical management includes organising software configuration management, and verification, validation and test activities.

2.2.5 Planning, scheduling and budgeting the work

Estimating the resources and time scales required for activities is a key part of planning their execution. The basic approach to estimation is to analyse the project into tasks that are small enough for their costs to be evaluated easily and accurately. Estimates for the time scales and resources for the whole project are then synthesised from the estimates for the individual tasks. Each task **should** be linked to an appropriate part of the deliverable for that phase. For example, tasks in the SR phase might be based on requirements, whereas in the AD phase they might be based on components. Traditionally, estimates for detailed design and production have been based on lines of code. Other factors that affect estimates are the experience of the development team, the novelty of the technical area and the availability of software engineering tools.

The Work Breakdown Structure (WBS) is one of the fundamental tools for the planning and control of project activities. The WBS describes the hierarchy of tasks (grouped into 'work packages') to be carried out in a project. The WBS corresponds to the structure of the work to be performed, and reflects the way in which the project costs will be summarised and reported.

A work package defines a set of tasks to be performed in a project. Work package descriptions **should** define tasks in sufficient detail to allow individuals, or small groups of people, to work independently of the rest of the project. The start and end dates of a work package **should** be specified. The duration of a product oriented work package **should** be sufficiently short to maintain visibility of the production process (e.g. a month in the DD phase). Procedure-oriented work packages, for example project management, may extend over the entire length of the project.

The work schedule **should** show when the work packages are to be started and finished. A milestone chart shows key events in the project; these **should** be related to work package completion dates.

An estimate of the cost of the whole project **should** be included in the SR phase section of the SPMP. Pending definition of the software requirements and the design, it will be difficult to provide accurate estimates. The actual costs of similar projects help in making initial estimates.

Cost models may be used for estimating the time required for detailed design and production. Careful consideration **should** be given to the applicability of any cost model. Parameter values attributed in making a cost model estimate **should** be clearly documented.

2.2.6   Reporting project progress

Project reporting is essential for the proper control of a software project. Carried out by project management, it provides visibility of development activity at regular intervals during the project. Reports are necessary to assure people outside the development team that the project is proceeding satisfactorily.

Project management **should** ensure that material presented at progress reviews is sufficiently detailed, and in a consistent format that enables the PHD to be compiled simply from progress-review data.

Contracts for software procurement **should** require that progress data be collected and progress reports be generated during the development. Any confidential material **should** be clearly marked as such.

2.3   THE SOFTWARE PROJECT MANAGEMENT PLAN

All software project management activities **shall** be documented in the Software Project Management Plan (SPMP). The SPMP is the controlling document for managing a software project. The SPMP is divided into four sections which contain the management plans for the SR, AD, DD and TR phases. The table of contents for each section of the SPMP is described in Appendix C. This table of contents is derived from the IEEE Standard for Software Project Management Plans (ANSI/IEEE Std 1058.1-1987).

2.4   EVOLUTION OF THE SPMP THROUGHOUT THE LIFE CYCLE

2.4.1   UR phase

By the end of the UR review, the SR phase section of the SPMP **shall** be produced (SPMP/SR). The SPMP/SR describes, in detail, the project activities to be carried out in the SR phase. As part of its introduction, the SPMP/SR **shall** outline a plan for the whole project.

A rough estimate of the total cost of the software project **should** be included in the SPMP/SR. Technical knowledge and experience gained on similar projects **should** be used in arriving at the cost estimate.

A precise estimate of the effort involved in the SR phase **shall** be included in the SPMP/SR. Specific factors affecting estimates for the work required in the SR phase are the:
- number of user requirements;
- level of user requirements;
- stability of user requirements;
- level of definition of external interfaces;
- quality of the URD.

An estimate based simply on the number of user requirements might be very misleading - a large number of detailed low-level user requirements might be more useful, and save more time in the SR phase, than a few high-level user requirements. A poor quality URD might imply that a lot of requirements analysis is required in the SR phase.

2.4.2   SR phase

During the SR phase, the AD phase section of the SPMP **shall** be produced (SPMP/AD). The SPMP/AD describes, in detail, the project activities to be carried out in the AD phase.

An estimate of the total project cost **shall** be included in the SPMP/AD. Technical knowledge and experience gained on similar projects **should** be used in arriving at this estimate.

When no similar projects exist, it may be useful to build a prototype, to get a more precise idea of the complexity of the software. Prototyping activities **should** be properly planned and resourced.

A precise estimate of the effort involved in the AD phase **shall** be included in the SPMP/AD. Specific factors that affect estimates for the work required in the AD phase are:

- number of software requirements;
- level of software requirements;
- stability of software requirements;
- level of definition of external interfaces;
- quality of the SRD.

If an evolutionary development life cycle approach is to be used, then this **should** be stated in the SPMP/AD.

2.4.3   AD phase

During the AD phase, the DD phase section of the SPMP **shall** be produced (SPMP/DD). The SPMP/DD describes, in detail, the project activities to be carried out in the DD phase.

An estimate of the total project cost **shall** be included in the SPMP/DD. The number of lines of code **should** be estimated for each software component. This **should** be used to estimate the time required to write the software, and therefore its cost.

The SPMP/DD **shall** contain a WBS that is directly related to the decomposition of the software into components.

The SPMP/DD **shall** contain a planning network showing the relationships between the coding, integration and testing activities. Tools are available for this kind of planning.

2.4.4   DD phase

As the detailed design work proceeds to lower levels, the WBS and job schedule need to be refined to reflect this. To achieve the necessary level of visibility, no software production work packages in the SPMP/DD **shall** last longer than 1 man-month.

During the DD phase, the TR phase section of the SPMP **shall** be produced (SPMP/TR). The SPMP/TR describes, in detail, project activities until final acceptance, in the OM phase.

CHAPTER 3
SOFTWARE CONFIGURATION MANAGEMENT

3.1 INTRODUCTION

As defined in ANSI/IEEE Std 610.12-1990, software configuration management (SCM) is the discipline of applying technical and administrative direction and surveillance to:

- identify and document the functional and physical characteristics of a configuration item;
- control changes to those characteristics;
- record and report change processing and implementation status;
- verify compliance with specified requirements[1].

Software configuration management is both a managerial and a technical activity, and is essential for proper software quality control. The software configuration management activities for a project must be defined in the Software Configuration Management Plan (SCMP).

All software items, for example documentation, source code, executable code, files, tools, test software and data, **shall** be subjected to configuration management procedures. The configuration management procedures **shall** establish methods for identifying, storing and changing software items through development, integration and transfer. In large developments, spread across multiple hardware platforms, configuration management procedures may differ in physical details. However, a common set of configuration management procedures **shall** be used.

Tools for software configuration management are widely available. Their use is strongly recommended to ensure that SCM procedures are applied consistently and efficiently.

---

1 Extracted from IEEE Std 610.12-1990, IEEE Glossary of Software Engineering Terminology, copyright © 1990 by the Institute of Electrical and Electronic Engineers, Inc. This information was written within the context of IEEE Std 610.12-1990, and the IEEE takes no responsibility for or liability for any damages resulting from the reader's misinterpretation of said information. This information does not represent the approved and consensus standard. Information is reproduced with the permission of the IEEE.

3.2 ACTIVITIES

3.2.1 Configuration identification

A 'configuration item' (CI) is an aggregation of hardware, software, or both, that is designated for configuration management and treated as a single entity in the configuration management process. Several factors may be relevant in deciding where to draw the boundaries of a configuration item. A configuration item may be any kind of software item, for example: a module, a document, or a set of CIs.

The key to effective software configuration management is unambiguous identification of the parts of the software. Every configuration item **shall** have an identifier that distinguishes it from other items with different:

- requirements, especially functionality and interfaces;
- implementation.

Each component defined in the design process **shall** be designated as a CI and possess an identifier. The identifier **shall** include a number or a name related to the purpose of the CI. The identifier **shall** include an indication of the type of processing the CI is intended for (e.g. filetype information).

The term 'version' is used to define a stage in the evolution of a CI. Each stage is marked by a 'version number'. When the CI changes, the version number changes. The identifier of a CI **shall** include a version number.

The identifier of documents **shall** include an issue number and a revision number. Issue numbers are used to mark major changes and revision numbers are used to mark minor changes. Major changes usually require formal approval. The issue number and revision number together mark the version of the document.

The configuration identification method **shall** be capable of accommodating new CIs, without requiring the modification of the identifiers of any existing CIs.

A 'baseline' is a document or a product that has been formally reviewed and agreed upon, and is a basis for further development. A baseline is an assembly of configuration items. Formal change control procedures are required to modify a baseline.

Integration of software **should** be coordinated by the identification and control of baselines. Figure 3.1 illustrates the relationship between units of modules, baselines and releases. Modules, after successful unit testing, are integrated into existing baselines. Incorporation into a baseline can only occur after successful integration tests. Baselines must be system tested before being transferred to users as a 'release' of the software. After delivery and installation, releases of the software undergo acceptance testing by users.

In the TR phase, a list of configuration items in the first release **shall** be included in the STD. In the OM phase, a list of changed configuration items **shall** be included in each Software Release Note (SRN). An SRN **shall** accompany each release made in the OM phase.

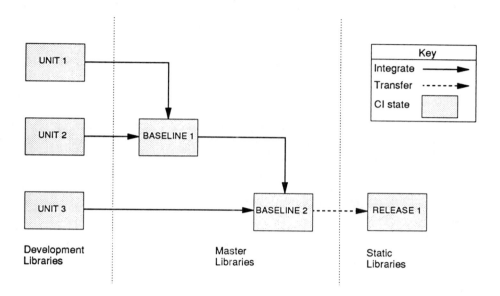

Figure 3.1 *Baselines and releases*

As part of the configuration identification method, a module **shall** have a header that includes:
- configuration item identifier (name, type, version);
- original author;
- creation date;
- change history (version/date/author/description);

Note that a module header may also contain other component information from the DDD, Part 2.

All documentation and storage media **shall** be clearly labelled in a standard format, with at least the following data:
- project name;
- configuration item identifier (name, type, version);
- date;
- content description.

3.2.2   Configuration item storage

A software library is a controlled collection of configuration items. It may be a single file or a collection of files. A library may exist on various media (e.g. paper, magnetic disk).

To ensure the security and control of the software, as a minimum, the following software libraries **shall** be implemented for storing all the deliverable components (e.g. documentation, source and executable code, test files, command procedures):

- Development (or Dynamic) library;
- Master (or Controlled) library;
- Static (or Archive) library.

Tools for handling software libraries are essential for efficient configuration control. Such tools **should** allow CI identification, change tracking, and CI cross-referencing.

Software is coded and tested as a set of modules in the development library. After unit tests, modules are transferred to master libraries for integration testing and system testing. When changes to master library modules are necessary, the appropriate modules are transferred back to a development library from the master library.

A baseline includes a set of master libraries. When a baseline is released, copies of all master libraries **should** be taken. These copies, called 'static' libraries, **shall** not be modified.

Up-to-date security copies of master and static libraries **shall** always be available. Procedures for the regular backup of development libraries **shall** be established. This is called 'media control'.

3.2.3 Configuration change control

Software configuration control is the process of evaluating proposed changes to configuration items and coordinating the implementation of approved changes. Software configuration control of an item can only occur after formal establishment of its configuration identification and inclusion in a baseline. Proper software configuration control demands the definition of the:

- level of authority required to change each CI;
- methods for handling proposals for changing any CI.

At the top level, the software configuration control process identifies the procedures for handling changes to known baselines.

In addition, project management has the responsibility for the organisation of SCM activities, the definition of SCM roles (e.g. configuration control board and software librarian), and the allocation of staff to those roles. In the TR and OM phases of a software project, ultimate responsibility for software configuration control lies with the Software Review Board (SRB). The SRB **should** be composed of members with sufficient authority and expertise to resolve any problems or nonconformances of the software.

When a software item does not conform to its specification, it **should** be identified as non-conforming, and held for review action. Nonconformance **should** be classified as minor or major depending on its severity and its urgency. Minor nonconformances can be processed at a level below SRB. Depending on the size and the management structure of the software development, a further classification **should** be performed in relation to the software life cycle, i.e. against the user requirements, software requirements, design, etc.

Changes to external interfaces or to software packages used by the system **should** be handled like changes to ordinary CIs.

3.2.3.1   Levels of change control

As a configuration item passes through unit, integration, system and acceptance tests, a higher level of authority is needed to approve changes. This is called the promotion of a CI. Just as programmers sign off unit tests, team leaders sign off integration tests, and project leaders sign off system tests, so change approval demands a level of authority corresponding to the verification status of the CI.

3.2.3.2   Change control procedures

Changes occur naturally in the evolution of the software system. This evolution **should** be planned and implemented using controlled software libraries. Changes can also occur because of problems in development or operation. Such changes require backtracking through the life cycle to ensure that the corrections are carried out with the same degree of quality control as was used for the original development. The level of authority for each change depends on the part to be changed, and on the phase in the life cycle that has been reached.

3.2.3.2.1   Documentation change procedures

The change procedure described below **shall** be observed when changes are needed to a delivered document.
1. A draft of a document is produced and submitted for review. If the document is not new, all changed text must be identified.
2. The reviewers record their comments about the draft document on Review Item Discrepancy (RID) forms. A recommended solution may be inserted on the RID form. The RIDs are then returned to the author(s) of the document.
3. The author(s) of the document record their response on the RID form.
4. Each RID is processed at a formal review meeting and an action decided (see Section 4.2.1).
5. The draft document and the approved RIDs are used to make the next revision, or issue if there major changes, of the document.
6. Each revision or issue of a document must be accompanied by a Document Change Record (DCR) and an updated Document Status Sheet (DSS).

Up to the end of the TR phase, the formal review meeting is a UR/R, SR/R, AD/R or DD/R, depending on the document. In the OM phase the formal review is conducted by the SRB. Templates for RID, DCR and DSS forms are provided in Appendix E.

3.2.3.2.2   Problem reporting procedures

Software problems can be reported at any stage in the life cycle. Problems can fall into a number of categories according to the degree of regression in the life cycle.

Problem categories are:

- operations error;
- user documentation does not conform to code;
- code does not conform to design;
- design does not conform to requirements;
- new or changed requirements.

Selection of the problem category defines the phase of the life cycle at which corrective action needs to start.

Software problems and change proposals **shall** be handled by the procedure described below. This change procedure requires a formal review to be held (see Section 4.2.1).

1. A Software Problem Report (SPR) must be completed for each detected problem, giving all information about the symptoms, the operating environment and the software under test. Evidence, such as listings of results, may be attached. A problem does not formally exist until an SPR has been written.

2. The SPR is passed to the Software Review Board (SRB) who will assign it to the relevant authority for analysis. A Software Change Request form (SCR) must be completed for each software change found necessary. This describes the changes required and includes an assessment of the cost and schedule impacts.

3. The Software Review Board then reviews each SCR and, if appropriate, assigns someone to carry out the change.

4. Each software modification is documented in detail in a Software Modification Report (SMR), complete with items such as:
   - source code changes;
   - test reports;
   - documentation changes;
   - verification reports.

Templates of SPR, SCR and SMR forms are given in Appendix E.

3.2.4 Configuration status accounting

Software configuration status accounting is the administrative tracking and reporting of all configuration items.

The status of all configuration items **shall** be recorded. Configuration status accounting continues, as do all other configuration management activities, throughout the life cycle.

To perform software status accounting, each software project **shall** record the:

- date and version/issue of each baseline;
- date and status of each RID and DCR;
- date and status of each SPR, SCR and SMR;
- summary description of each Configuration Item.

Configuration status accounts **should** be produced at project milestones, and may be produced periodically between project milestones.

Information in configuration status accounts **should** be used to generate the SRNs and CI lists that must accompany each delivery of a software baseline.

3.2.5 Release

The first release of the software must be documented in the STD. Subsequent releases of software must be accompanied by a Software Release Note (SRN) that lists the CIs included in the release, and the procedures for installing them, so that they can be made available for use (see Appendix E). As a minimum, the SRN **shall** record the faults that have been repaired and the new requirements that have been incorporated.

For each release, documentation and code **shall** be consistent. Further, old releases **shall** be retained, for reference. Where possible, the previous release **should** be kept online during a change-over period, to allow comparisons, and as a fallback. Older releases may be archived. The number of releases in operational use at any time **should** be minimised.

Some form of software protection is desirable for controlled source and binary code to avoid use of an incorrect release. The strength of this protection depends on the criticality of use of the product. In general, each release **should** be self-identifying (e.g. checksum, operator dialogue or printed output).

Modified software **shall** be retested before release. Tests **should** be selected from the SVVP to demonstrate its operational capability.

While it is usually not necessary to repeat all the acceptance tests after a software change is made, a standard subset of the acceptance tests (often called 'regression tests') **should** be run when any new release is made. These tests are required to demonstrate that a modification has introduced no unexpected side effects.

3.3 THE SOFTWARE CONFIGURATION MANAGEMENT PLAN

All software configuration management activities **shall** be documented in the Software Configuration Management Plan (SCMP). The SCMP is divided into four sections which contain the configuration management plans for the SR, AD, DD and TR phases. The table of contents for each section of SCMP is described in Appendix C. This table of contents is derived from the IEEE Standard for Software Configuration Management Plans (ANSI/IEEE Std 828-1990).

Additional information on configuration management may be found in ANSI/IEEE Std 1042-1987, Guide to Software Configuration Management.

3.4 EVOLUTION OF THE SCMP THROUGHOUT THE LIFE CYCLE

Configuration management procedures **shall** be in place before software production (code and documentation) starts. SCM procedures **should** be simple and efficient. Wherever possible, procedures **should** be capable of reuse in later phases. Instability in SCM procedures can be a major cause of poor progress in a software project.

3.4.1 UR phase

By the end of the UR review, the SR phase section of the SCMP **shall** be produced (SCMP/SR). The SCMP/SR **shall** cover the configuration management procedures for all documentation, CASE tool outputs or prototype code, to be produced in the SR phase.

3.4.2 SR phase

During the SR phase, the AD phase section of the SCMP **shall** be produced (SCMP/AD). The SCMP/AD **shall** cover the configuration management procedures for documentation, CASE tool outputs or prototype code, to be produced in the AD phase. Unless there is a good reason to change (e.g. different CASE tool used), SR phase procedures **should** be reused.

3.4.3 AD phase

During the AD phase, the DD phase section of the SCMP **shall** be produced (SCMP/DD). The SCMP/DD **shall** cover the configuration management procedures for documentation, deliverable code, CASE tool outputs or prototype code, to be produced in the DD phase. Unless there is a good reason to change, AD or SR phase procedures **should** be reused.

3.4.4 DD phase

During the DD phase, the TR phase section of the SCMP **shall** be produced (SCMP/TR). The SCMP/TR **shall** cover the procedures for the configuration management of the deliverables in the operational environment.

CHAPTER 4
SOFTWARE VERIFICATION AND VALIDATION

4.1 INTRODUCTION

The term 'verification' has several meanings depending upon the context. Three common meanings are:

- act of reviewing, inspecting, testing, checking, auditing, or otherwise establishing and documenting whether or not items, processes, services or documents conform to specified requirements (ANSI/ASQC A3-1978, Quality Systems Terminology);
- process of evaluating a system or component to determine whether the products of a given development phase satisfy the conditions imposed at the start of that phase (ANSI/IEEE Std 610.12-1990)[2];
- formal proof of program correctness (ANSI/IEEE Std 610.12-1990).

The first definition of verification in the list above is the most general and includes the other two. In these Standards, the first definition (ANSI/ASQC A3-1978) applies.

Validation is, according to its ANSI/IEEE definition, 'the evaluation of software at the end of the software development process to ensure compliance with the user requirements'. Validation is, therefore, 'end-to-end' verification.

Verification is essential for assuring the quality of a product. Software verification is both a managerial and a technical function, since the verification programme needs to be both defined and implemented. A project's verification activities **should** reflect the software's criticality, and the quality required of it. Verification can be the most time-consuming and expensive part of a project; verification activities **should** appear in the SPMP. Figure 4.1 shows the life cycle verification approach.

---

2 Extracted from IEEE Std 610.12-1990, IEEE Glossary of Software Engineering Terminology, copyright © 1990 by the Institute of Electrical and Electronic Engineers, Inc. This information was written within the context of IEEE Std 610.12-1990, and the IEEE takes no responsibility for or liability for any damages resulting from the reader's misinterpretation of said information. This information does not represent the approved and consensus standard. Information is reproduced with the permission of the IEEE.

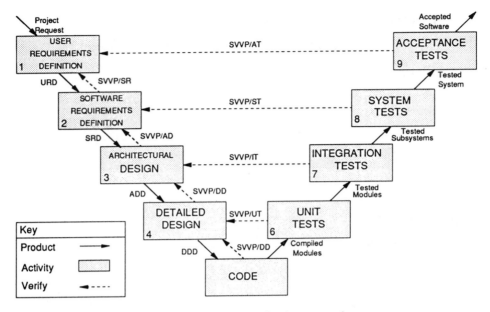

Figure 4.1 *Life cycle verification approach*

4.2   ACTIVITIES

Verification activities include:
- technical reviews, walkthroughs and software inspections;
- checking that software requirements are traceable to user requirements;
- checking that design components are traceable to software requirements;
- checking formal proofs and algorithms;
- unit testing;
- integration testing;
- system testing;
- acceptance testing;
- audits.

The actual activities to be conducted in a project are described in the Software Verification and Validation Plan (SVVP).

As well as demonstrating that assertions about the software are true, verification can also show that assertions are false. The skill and ingenuity needed to identify defects **should** not be underestimated. Users will have more confidence in a product that has been through a rigorous verification programme than one subjected to minimal examination and testing before release.

4.2.1 Reviews

The procedures for software reviews are based closely on the ANSI/IEEE Std 1028-1988. A software review is an evaluation of a software element to ascertain discrepancies from planned results and to recommend improvements.

Three kinds of reviews can be used for software verification:

- technical review;
- walkthrough;
- software inspection.

The three kinds of reviews are all 'formal reviews' in the sense that all have specific objectives and procedures. All kinds of review seek to identify defects and discrepancies of the software against specifications, plans and standards.

The software problem reporting procedure and document change procedure defined in Part 2, Section 3.2.3.2, call for a formal review process for all changes to code and documentation. Any of the three kinds of formal review procedure can be applied for change control. The SRB, for example, may choose to perform a technical review, software inspection or walkthrough as necessary.

4.2.1.1 Technical reviews

Technical reviews **should** be used for the UR/R, SR/R, AD/R, and DD/R. Technical reviews evaluate specific software elements to verify progress against plan.

The objective of a technical review is to evaluate a specific software element (e.g. document, source module), and provide management with evidence that:

- it conforms to specifications made in previous phases;
- the software element has been produced according to the project standards and procedures;
- changes have been properly implemented, and affect only those systems areas identified by the change specification (described in a DCR or SCR).

4.2.1.2 Walkthroughs

Walkthroughs **should** be used for the early evaluation of documents, models, designs and code in the SR, AD and DD phases.

The objective of a walkthrough is to evaluate a specific software element (e.g. document, source module). A walkthrough **should** attempt to identify defects and consider possible solutions. In contrast with other forms of review, secondary objectives are to educate, and to resolve stylistic problems.

4.2.1.3 Software inspections

Software inspections **should** be used for the evaluation of documents and code in the SR, AD and DD phases, before technical review or testing.

The objective of a software inspection is to detect and identify defects. A software inspection is a rigorous peer examination that:

- identifies nonconformances with respect to specifications and standards;

- uses metrics to monitor progress;
- ignores stylistic issues;
- does not discuss solutions.

4.2.2 Tracing

Forwards traceability requires that each input to a phase **shall** be traceable to an output of that phase. Forwards traceability demonstrates completeness. Forwards tracing is normally done by constructing cross-reference matrices. Holes in the matrix demonstrate incompleteness quite vividly.

Backwards traceability requires that each output of a phase **shall** be traceable to an input to that phase. Outputs that cannot be traced to inputs are superfluous, unless it is acknowledged that the inputs themselves were incomplete. Backwards tracing is normally done by including with each item a statement of why it exists (e.g. the description of the function of a component may be a list of functional requirements).

During the software life cycle it is necessary to trace:

- user requirements to software requirements and vice-versa;
- software requirements to component descriptions and vice versa;
- integration tests to major components of the architecture and vice-versa;
- system tests to software requirements and vice-versa;
- acceptance tests to user requirements and vice-versa.

To support traceability, all components and requirements are identified. The SVVP **should** define how tracing is to be done. References to components and requirements **should** include identifiers.

4.2.3 Formal proof

Where practical, formal deductive proof of the correctness of software may be attempted.

Formal Methods, such as Z and VDM, possess an agreed notation, with well-defined semantics, and a calculus, which allows proofs to be constructed. The first property is shared with other methods for software specification, but the second sets them apart. If a Formal Method can demonstrate with certainty that something is correct, then separate verification is not necessary. However, human errors are still possible, and ways **should** be sought to avoid them, for example by ensuring that all proofs are checked independently. CASE tools are available that support Formal Methods, and their use is recommended.

Refinement of a formal specification into executable code is generally not a deductive process; other forms of verification (e.g. testing), are necessary to verify the refinement.

4.2.4 Testing

Testing is the process of exercising or evaluating a system or system component, by manual or automated means, to:

- confirm that it satisfies specified requirements;
- identify differences between expected and actual results.

The amount of time spent in testing software is frequently underestimated. Testing activities must be carefully specified so that they can be adequately budgeted for. The expense of testing increases with the number of errors present before it begins. Cheaper methods of removing errors, such as inspection, walkthrough and formal proof, **should** always be tried before testing is started.

Software testing includes the following activities:
- planning the general approach and allocating resources;
- detailing the general approach for various kinds of tests in a test design;
- defining the inputs, predicted results and execution conditions in a test case specification;
- stating the sequence of actions to be carried out by test personnel in a test procedure;
- logging the execution of a test procedure in a test report.

Four kinds of testing have been identified in these Standards: unit testing, integration testing, system testing and acceptance testing.

Test software **should** be produced to the same standards as the deliverable software. Test software and data must therefore be documented and subjected to configuration control procedures. This allows monitoring of the testing process, and permits test software and data to be reused later, to verify that the software's functionality and performance have not been impaired by modifications. This is called 'regression' testing.

Test plans, test designs, test cases, test procedures and test reports for unit, integration, system and acceptance tests must be documented in the SVVP. Figure 4.2 summarises when and where testing is documented in the SVVP.

In Figure 4.2, the entry 'Plans' in the System Tests row, for example, means that the System Test Plans are drawn up in the SR phase and placed in the SVVP section 'System Tests', subsection 'Plans'. This is abbreviated as 'SVVP/ST/Plans'.

Reports of Acceptance Tests must also be summarised in the Software Transfer Document.

PHASE SVVP SECTION	USER REQUIREMENTS REVIEW	SOFTWARE REQUIREMENTS DEFINITION	ARCHITECTURAL DESIGN	DETAILED DESIGN AND PRODUCTION	TRANSFER
ACCEPTANCE TESTS	Plans			Designs Cases Procedures	Reports
SYSTEM TESTS		Plans		Designs Cases Procedures Reports	
INTEGRATION TESTS			Plans	Designs Cases Procedures Reports	
UNIT TESTS				Plans Designs Cases Procedures Reports	

Figure 4.2 *Life cycle production of test documentation*

4.2.5 Auditing

Audits are independent reviews that assess compliance with software requirements, specifications, baselines, standards, procedures, instructions, codes and contractual and licensing requirements. A 'physical audit' checks that all items identified as being part of the configuration are present in the product baseline. A 'functional audit' checks that unit, integration and system tests have been carried out and records their success or failure. Functional and physical audits **shall** be performed before the release of the software.

4.3 THE SOFTWARE VERIFICATION AND VALIDATION PLAN

All software verification and validation activities **shall** be documented in the Software Verification and Validation Plan (SVVP). The SVVP is divided into seven sections which contain the verification plans for the SR, AD, DD phases and the unit, integration, system and acceptance test specifications. The table of contents for each section of SVVP is described in Appendix C. This table of contents is derived from the IEEE Standard for Verification and Validation Plans (IEEE Std 1012-1986) and the IEEE Standard for Software Test Documentation (IEEE Std 829-1983).

The SVVP **shall** ensure that the verification activities:
* are appropriate for the degree of criticality of the software;
* meet the verification and acceptance testing requirements (stated in the SRD);
* verify that the product will meet the quality, reliability, maintainability and safety requirements (stated in the SRD);
* are sufficient to assure the quality of the product.

4.4 EVOLUTION OF THE SVVP THROUGHOUT THE LIFE CYCLE

4.4.1 UR phase

By the end of the UR review, the SR phase section of the SVVP **shall** be produced (SVVP/SR). The SVVP/SR **shall** define how to trace user requirements to software requirements, so that each software requirement can be justified. It **should** describe how the SRD is to be evaluated by defining the review procedures. It may include specifications of the tests to be performed with prototypes.

The initiator(s) of the user requirements **should** lay down the principles upon which the acceptance tests **should** be based. The developer **shall** construct an acceptance test plan in the UR phase and document it in the SVVP. This plan **should** define the scope, approach, resources and schedule of acceptance testing activities.

4.4.2 SR phase

During the SR phase, the AD phase section of the SVVP **shall** be produced (SVVP/AD). The SVVP/AD **shall** define how to trace software requirements to components, so that each software component can be justified. It **should** describe how the ADD is to be evaluated by defining the review procedures. It may include specifications of the tests to be performed with prototypes.

During the SR Phase, the developer analyses the user requirements and may insert 'Acceptance testing requirements' in the SRD. These requirements constrain the design of the acceptance tests. This must be recognised in the statement of the purpose and scope of the acceptance tests.

The planning of the system tests **should** proceed in parallel with the definition of the software requirements. The developer may identify 'Verification requirements' for the software - these are additional constraints on the unit, integration and system testing activities. These requirements are also stated in the SRD.

The developer **shall** construct a system test plan in the SR phase and document it in the SVVP. This plan **should** define the scope, approach, resources and schedule of system testing activities.

4.4.3   AD phase

During the AD phase, the DD phase section of the SVVP **shall** be produced (SVVP/DD). The SVVP/AD **shall** describe how the DDD and code are to be evaluated by defining the review and traceability procedures.

The developer **shall** construct an integration test plan in the AD phase and document it in the SVVP. This plan **should** describe the scope, approach, resources and schedule of intended integration tests. Note that the items to be integrated are the software components described in the ADD.

4.4.4   DD phase

In the DD phase, the SVVP sections on testing are developed as the detailed design and implementation information become available.

The developer **shall** construct a unit test plan in the DD phase and document it in the SVVP. This plan **should** describe the scope, approach, resources and schedule of intended unit tests. The items to be tested are the software components described in the DDD.

The unit, integration, system and acceptance test designs **shall** be described in the SVVP. These **should** specify the details of the test approach for a software feature, or combination of software features, and identify the associated tests.

The unit integration, system and acceptance test cases **shall** be described in the SVVP. These **should** specify the inputs, predicted results and execution conditions for a test item.

The unit, integration, system and acceptance test procedures **shall** be described in the SVVP. These **should** be provide a step-by-step description of how to carry out each test case.

The unit, integration, system and acceptance test reports **shall** be contained in the SVVP.

CHAPTER 5
SOFTWARE QUALITY ASSURANCE

5.1 INTRODUCTION

Software Quality Assurance (SQA) is 'a planned and systematic pattern of all actions necessary to provide adequate confidence that the item or product conforms to established technical requirements' (ANSI/IEEE Std 730-1989). Software Quality Assurance is synonymous with Software 'Product Assurance' (PA) and the terms are used interchangeably in these Standards.

The quality assurance activity is the process of verifying that these Standards are being applied. In small projects this could be done by the development team, but in large projects specific staff **should** be allocated to the role.

The Software Quality Assurance Plan (SQAP) defines how adherence to these Standards will be monitored. The SQAP contents list is a checklist for activities that have to be carried out to assure the quality of the product. For each activity, those with responsibility for SQA **should** describe the plans for monitoring it.

5.2 ACTIVITIES

Objective evidence of adherence to these Standards **should** be sought during all phases of the life cycle. Documents called for by this standard **should** be obtained and examined. Source code **should** be checked for adherence to coding standards. Where possible, aspects of quality (e.g. complexity, reliability, maintainability, safety, number of defects, number of problems, number of RIDs) **should** be measured quantitatively, using well-established metrics.

Subsequent sections list activities derived from ANSI/IEEE Std 730-1989 that are necessary if a software item is to be fit for its purpose. Each section discusses how the activity can be verified.

5.2.1 Management

Analysis of the managerial structure that influences and controls the quality of the software is an SQA activity. The existence of an appropriate organisational structure

should be verified. It **should** be confirmed that the individuals defined in that structure have defined tasks and responsibilities. The organisation, tasks and responsibilities will have been defined in the SPMP.

5.2.2 Documentation

The documentation plan that has been defined in the SPMP **should** be analysed. Any departures from the documentation plan defined in these Standards **should** be scrutinised and discussed with project management.

5.2.3 Standards, practices, conventions and metrics

Adherence to all standards, practices and conventions **should** be monitored. Deviations and non-conformance **should** be noted and brought to the attention of project management. SQA personnel may assist project management with the correct interpretation of standards, practices and conventions.

A 'metric' is a quantitative measure of the degree to which a system, component, or process possesses a given attribute. Metrics are essential for effective management. Metrics need to be simple to understand and apply to be useful.

Metrics for measuring quality, particularly reliability, and maintainability, **should** be specified in the SRD. These metrics **should** be meaningful to users, and reflect their requirements. Additional metrics may be defined by the project. Values of complexity metrics may be defined in the design standards to limit design complexity, for example. Metrics may be defined in the SPMP to guide decision-making (e.g. if a software component exhibits more than three failures in integration testing then it will be reinspected).

Metrics **should** relate to project objectives, so that they can be used for controlling it. All objectives **should** have metrics attached to them, otherwise undue weight can be given to those for which metrics have been defined. A project that counts the number of lines of code written, but not the failure rate, is likely to concentrate on producing a large volume of code, and not reliability, for example.

5.2.4 Reviews and audits

These Standards call for reviews of the URD, the SRD, the ADD, the DDD, the SVVP and the SCMP. It also calls for the review and audit of the code during production. The review and audit arrangements described in the SVVP **should** be examined. Many kinds of reviews are possible (e.g. technical, inspection and walkthrough). It **should** be verified that the review mechanisms are appropriate for the type of project. SQA personnel **should** participate in the review process.

5.2.5 Testing activities

Unit, integration, system and acceptance testing of executable software is essential to assure its quality. Test plans, test designs, test case, test procedures and test reports are described in the SVVP. These **should** be reviewed by SQA personnel. They **should** monitor the testing activities carried out by the development team, including test execution. Additionally, other tests may be proposed in the SQAP. These may be carried out by SQA personnel.

5.2.6 Problem reporting and corrective action

The problem handling procedure described in these Standards is designed to report and track problems from identification until solution. SQA personnel **should** monitor the execution of the procedures, described in the SCMP, and examine trends in problem occurrence.

5.2.7 Tools, techniques and methods

These Standards call for tools, techniques and methods for software production to be defined at the project level. It is an SQA activity to check that appropriate tools, techniques and methods are selected and to monitor their correct application.

SQA personnel may decide that additional tools, techniques and methods are required to support their monitoring activity. These **should** be described in the SQAP.

5.2.8 Code and media control

These Standards require that the procedures for the methods and facilities used to maintain, store, secure and document controlled versions of the identified software, be defined in the SCMP. SQA personnel **should** check that appropriate procedures have been defined in the SCMP and carried out.

5.2.9 Supplier control

Software items acquired from external suppliers must always be checked against the standards for the project. An SQAP **shall** be produced by each contractor developing software. An SQAP is not required for commercial software.

5.2.10 Records collection, maintenance and retention

These standards define a set of documents that must be produced in any project. Additional documents, for example minutes of meetings and review records, may also be produced. SQA personnel **should** check that appropriate methods and facilities are used to assemble, safeguard, and maintain all this documentation for at least the life of the project. Documentation control procedures are defined in the SCMP.

5.2.11 Training

SQA personnel **should** check that development staff are properly trained for their tasks and identify any training that is necessary. Training plans are documented in the SPMP.

5.2.12 Risk management

All projects must identify the factors that are critical to their success and control these factors. This is called 'risk management'. Project management must always analyse the risks that affect the project. Their findings are documented in the SPMP. SQA personnel **should** monitor the risk management activity, and advise project management on the methods and procedures to identify, assess, monitor, and control areas of risk.

5.3   THE SOFTWARE QUALITY ASSURANCE PLAN

All software quality assurance activities **shall** be documented in the Software Quality Assurance Plan (SQAP). The recommended table of contents for the SQAP is presented in Appendix C. This table of contents is derived from the IEEE Standard for Software Quality Assurance Plans (ANSI/IEEE Std 730-1989).

5.4   EVOLUTION OF THE SQAP THROUGHOUT THE LIFE CYCLE

5.4.1   UR phase

By the end of the UR review, the SR phase section of the SQAP **shall** be produced (SQAP/SR). The SQAP/SR **shall** describe, in detail, the quality assurance activities to be carried out in the SR phase. The SQAP/SR **shall** outline the quality assurance plan for the rest of the project.

5.4.2   SR phase

During the SR phase, the AD phase section of the SQAP **shall** be produced (SQAP/AD). The SQAP/AD **shall** cover in detail all the quality assurance activities to be carried out in the AD phase.

In the SR phase, the SRD **should** be analysed to extract any constraints that relate to software quality assurance (e.g. standards and documentation requirements).

5.4.3   AD phase

During the AD phase, the DD phase section of the SQAP **shall** be produced (SQAP/DD). The SQAP/DD **shall** cover in detail all the quality assurance activities to be carried out in the DD phase.

5.4.4   DD phase

During the DD phase, the TR phase section of the SQAP **shall** be produced (SQAP/TR). The SQAP/TR **shall** cover in detail all the quality assurance activities to be carried out from the start of the TR phase until final acceptance in the OM phase.

Part Three

Appendices

APPENDIX A
GLOSSARY

A.1   LIST OF TERMS

The terminology used in these Standards conforms to ANSI/IEEE Std 610.12-1990, 'IEEE Standard Glossary of Software Engineering Terminology'. This section contains definitions of terms:

- that are not contained in ANSI/IEEE Std 610.12-1990;
- that have multiple definitions in ANSI/IEEE Std 610.12-1990, one of which is used in these Standards (denoted by *).

Component
General term for a part of a software system. Components may be assembled and decomposed to form new components. They are implemented as modules, tasks or programs, any of which may be configuration items. This usage of the term is more general than in ANSI/IEEE parlance, which defines a component as a 'basic part of a system or program'; in these Standards, components may not be 'basic' as they can be decomposed.

Concurrent Production and Documentation
A technique of software development where the documentation of a module proceeds in parallel with its production, i.e. detailed design specifications, coding and testing.

Decomposition
The breaking down into parts.

Development
The period from URD delivery to final acceptance, during which the software is produced.

Developer
The person or organisation responsible for developing the software from a specification of the user requirements to an operational system.

Environment
Either: Physical conditions such as temperature, humidity and cleanliness, within which a computer system operates; or, the support and utility software and hardware.

Formal Method
A mathematically precise means of specifying software, enabling specifications to be proven consistent.

Interface Control Document
A specification of an interface between a system and an external system.

Layer
One hierarchical level in the decomposition of a system.

Logical model
An implementation-independent representation of a real world process; contrast physical model.

Model
A representation of a real world process. A software model is composed of symbols organised according to some convention.

Maintainability
The ease with which software can be maintained (*).

Nonconformance
A statement of conflict between descriptive documentation and the object described.

Physical model
An implementation-dependent representation of a real world process; contrast logical model.

Production
The process of writing and testing software, as opposed to design and operations.

Project
Either the development process or the organisation devoted to the development process.

Prototype
An executable model of selected aspects of a proposed system.

Recognised method
Describes the characteristics of an agreed process or procedure used in the engineering of a product or performing a service.

Release
A baseline made available for use.

Reliability
The probability that software will not cause the failure of a system for a specified time under specified conditions.

Review
An activity to verify that the outputs of a phase in the software life cycle conform to their specifications (contrast IEEE: 'Design Review'.)

Stability
Quality of not changing. Either in the short term, not breaking down, or in the longer term, not subject to design and/or requirements changes (Contrast IEEE (1) the ability to continue unchanged despite disturbing or disruptive events, (2) the ability to return to an original state after disturbing or disruptive events).

Task
A software component that executes sequentially. A task may execute in parallel with other tasks.

Traceability
The ability to relate an input to a phase of the software life cycle to an output from that phase. The item may be code or documentation.

Traceability Matrix
Matrix showing which outputs correspond to which inputs. More often showing which parts of a design satisfy which requirements.

Trade-off
Comparison of alternatives to determine the optimal solution.

User
Any individual or group ultimately making use of the output from a computer system, distinct from personnel responsible for building, operating or maintaining the system.

Verification
The act of reviewing, inspecting, testing, checking, auditing, or otherwise establishing and documenting whether items, processes, services or documents conform to specified requirements (ANSI/ASQC A3-1978 Quality Systems Terminology).

Version
A stage in the evolution of a configuration item.

Work-Around
A temporary solution to a problem.

Work Breakdown Structure
The WBS describes the hierarchy of tasks (grouped into 'work packages') to be carried out in a project. The WBS corresponds to the structure of the work to be performed, and reflects the way in which the project costs will be summarised and reported.

Work Package
A detailed, short span, unit of work to be performed in a project.

A.2   LIST OF ACRONYMS

AD	Architectural Design
ADD	Architectural Design Document
AD/R	Architectural Design Review
ANSI	American National Standards Institute
AT	Acceptance Test
CASE	Computer Aided Software Engineering
DCR	Document Change Record
DD	Detailed Design and production
DDD	Detailed Design and production Document
DD/R	Detailed Design and production Review
DSS	Document Status Sheet
IEEE	Institute of Electrical and Electronics Engineers
ICD	Interface Control Document
IT	Integration Test
PA	Product Assurance
PHD	Project History Document
PSS	Procedures, Specifications and Standards
QA	Quality Assurance
RID	Review Item Discrepancy
SCM	Software Configuration Management
SCMP	Software Configuration Management Plan
SCR	Software Change Request
SPM	Software Project Management
SPMP	Software Project Management Plan
SMR	Software Modification Report
SPR	Software Problem Report
SQA	Software Quality Assurance
SQAP	Software Quality Assurance Plan
SR	Software Requirements
SRB	Software Review Board
SRD	Software Requirements Document
SRN	Software Release Note
SR/R	Software Requirements Review
ST	System Test
STD	Software Transfer Document
SUM	Software User Manual
SVVP	Software Verification and Validation Plan
UR	User Requirements
URD	User Requirements Document
UR/R	User Requirements Review
UT	Unit Tests

APPENDIX B
SOFTWARE PROJECT DOCUMENTS

This Appendix summarises the documents that can be produced in a software engineering project. Table B.1 summarises technical documents. Table B.2 summarises the plans. Table B.3 summarises reports, forms and other documentation.

Acronym	Name	Purpose
URD	User Requirements Document	To state the needs of the users of the software system.
SRD	Software Requirements Document	To specify the requirements of the software system from the developer's point of view. The SRD incorporates the user requirements described in the URD.
ADD	Architectural Design Document	To specify the top-level components of the software. The ADD fulfils the software requirements stated in the SRD.
DDD	Detailed Design Document	To specify the lower-level components of the software. The DDD fulfils the requirements laid down in the SRD, following the top-level design described in the ADD.
SUM	Software User Manual	To state what the software does and how to operate the software.
STD	Software Transfer Document	To contain the checked configuration item list and SPRs, SCRs, SMRs generated in the TR phase
PHD	Project History Document	To record significant information about the specification, design, production and operation of the software.

Table B.1 *Summary of technical documents*

Acronym	Name	Purpose
SPMP	Software Project Management Plan	To state the organisation, WBS, schedule and budget, for each development phase.
SCMP	Software Configuration Management Plan	To state the procedures for identifying, controlling, and recording the status of software items.
SVVP	Software Verification and Validation Plan	To state the procedures for testing the software and for verifying that the products of each phase are consistent with their inputs.
SQAP	Software Quality Assurance Plan	To state the procedures for assuring the quality of the software products.

Table B.2 *Summary of plans required*

Acronym	Name	Purpose
DCR	Document Change Record	To record a set of changes to a document.
DSS	Document Status Sheet	To summarise the issues and revisions of a document.
RID	Review Item Discrepancy	To state issues to be addressed in a review and record decisions made.
SCR	Software Change Request	To describe changes required in the software and its documentation in the TR and OM phases, including new requirements.
SMR	Software Modification Report	To describe changes made to the software and its documentation in the TR and OM phases.
SPR	Software Problem Report	To record a problem reported in the use or test of software and its documentation.
SRN	Software Release Note	To summarise changes made to software with respect to the previous release.

Table B.3 *Summary of reports and forms*

APPENDIX C
DOCUMENT TEMPLATES

All documents **should** contain the following service information:

   a - Abstract
   b - Table of contents
   c - Document Status Sheet
   d - Document Change Records made since last issue

If there is no information pertinent to a section, the following **should** appear below the section heading: 'This section not applicable', with the appropriate reasons for this exclusion.

Guidelines on the contents of document sections are given in *italics*. Section titles which are to be provided by document authors are enclosed in square brackets.

C.1 URD table of contents[3]

1   Introduction
 1.1 Purpose of the document
 1.2 Scope of the software
 1.3 Definitions, acronyms and abbreviations
 1.4 References
 1.5 Overview of the document

2   General Description
 2.1   Product perspective
   Describe related external systems and subsystems.
 2.2   General capabilities
   Describe the main capabilities required and why they are needed.
 2.3   General constraints
   Describe the main constraints that apply and why they exist.
 2.4   User characteristics
   Describe who will use the software and when.
 2.5   Operational environment
   Describe what external systems do and their interfaces with the product.
 2.6   Assumptions and dependencies
   Describe the assumptions upon which the requirements depend.

3   Specific Requirements
 List the specific requirements, with attributes.
 3.1   Capability requirements
 3.2   Constraint requirements

---

3 Extracted from IEEE Std 830-1984, IEEE Guide for Software Requirements Specifications, copyright © 1984 by the Institute of Electrical and Electronic Engineers, Inc. This information was written within the context of IEEE Std 830-1984, and the IEEE takes no responsibility for or liability for any damages resulting from the reader's misinterpretation of said information. This information does not represent the approved and consensus standard. Information is reproduced with the permission of the IEEE.

C.2 SRD table of contents [4]

1 Introduction
  1.1 Purpose of the document
  1.2 Scope of the software
  1.3 Definitions, acronyms and abbreviations
  1.4 References
  1.5 Overview of the document

2 General Description
  2.1 Relation to current projects
    Describe the relationship to other current projects.
  2.2 Relation to predecessor and successor projects
    Describe the relationship to previous and future projects.
  2.3 Function and purpose
    Describe the main functions the product must perform.
  2.4 Environmental considerations
    Describe where the product will be used, who will use it, who will operate it, the hardware it will run on, and the operating system.
  2.5 Relation to other systems
    Describe related external systems and subsystems.
  2.6 General constraints
    Describe the main constraints that apply and why they exist.
  2.7 Model description
    Describe the logical model using a recognised analysis method.

3 Specific Requirements
  List the specific requirements, with attributes.
  Subsections may be regrouped around high-level functions.
  3.1 Functional requirements
  3.2 Performance requirements
  3.3 Interface requirements
  3.4 Operational requirements
  3.5 Resource requirements
  3.6 Verification requirements
  3.7 Acceptance testing requirements
  3.8 Documentation requirements
  3.9 Security requirements

---

4 Extracted from IEEE Std 830-1984, IEEE Guide for Software Requirements Specifications, copyright © 1984 by the Institute of Electrical and Electronic Engineers, Inc. This information was written within the context of IEEE Std 830-1984, and the IEEE takes no responsibility for or liability for any damages resulting from the reader's misinterpretation of said information. This information does not represent the approved and consensus standard. Information is reproduced with the permission of the IEEE.

3.10 Portability requirements
3.11 Quality requirements
3.12 Reliability requirements
3.13 Maintainability requirements
3.14 Safety requirements

4   User Requirements vs Software Requirements Traceability matrix
Give a table cross-referencing software requirements to user requirements.

C.3 ADD table of contents[5]

1 Introduction
   1.1 Purpose of the document
   1.2 Scope of the software
   1.3 Definitions, acronyms and abbreviations
   1.4 References
   1.5 Overview of the document

2 System Overview
Summarise the system context and system design.

3 System Context
Describe the system context, with diagrams.
Define the external interfaces.

4 System Design
   4.1 Design method
      Describe or reference the design method.
   4.2 Decomposition description
      Describe the system design, with diagrams.
      Show the components and the control and data flow between them.

5 Component Description
Describe each component.
Structure this section according to the design.
   5.n [Component identifier]
      5.n.1 Type
         Say whether the component is a module, a file, a program etc
      5.n.2 Purpose
         Trace the component to the software requirements.
      5.n.3 Function
         Say what the component does.
      5.n.4 Subordinates
         List the immediate children.
      5.n.5 Dependencies
         Describe the preconditions for using this component.

---

5 Extracted from IEEE Std 1016-1987, IEEE Recommended Practice for Software Design Descriptions, copyright © 1987 by the Institute of Electrical and Electronic Engineers, Inc. This information was written within the context of IEEE Std 1016-1987, and the IEEE takes no responsibility for or liability for any damages resulting from the reader's misinterpretation of said information. This information does not represent the approved and consensus standard. Information is reproduced with the permission of the IEEE.

5.n.6   Interfaces
Define the control and data flow to and from the component.

5.n.7   Resources
List the resources required, such as displays and printers.

5.n.8   References
Reference any documents needed to understand the component.

5.n.9   Processing
Describe the control and data flow within the component.
Outline the processing of bottom-level components.

5.n.10 Data
Define in detail the data internal to components, such as files, used for interfacing major components.
Otherwise give an outline description.

6   Feasibility and Resource Estimates
Summarise the computer resources required to build, operate and maintain the software.

7   Software Requirements vs Components Traceability matrix
Give a table cross-referencing components to software requirements.

C.4 DDD table of contents [6]

Part 1 - General Description
   1   Introduction
      1.1   Purpose of the document
      1.2   Scope of the software
      1.3   Definitions, acronyms and abbreviations
      1.4   References
      1.5   Overview of the document

   2   Project Standards, Conventions and Procedures
      2.1   Design standards
          Describe or reference the design method used.
      2.2   Documentation standards
          Describe the format, style and tools for documentation.
      2.3   Naming conventions
          Describe the conventions for naming files, modules etc.
      2.4   Programming standards
          Define and reference the coding standards.
      2.5   Software development tools
          Define and reference the design and production tools.

Part 2 - Component Design Specifications
Describe each component.
Structure this section according to the design.
   n   [Component identifier]
        Give the name of the component.
      n.1   Type
          Say whether the component is a module, a file, a program etc.
      n.2   Purpose
          Trace the component to the software requirements.
      n.3   Function
          Say what the component does.
      n.4   Subordinates
          List the immediate children.
      n.5   Dependencies
          Describe the preconditions for using this component.

---

6 Extracted from IEEE Std 1016-1987, IEEE Recommended Practice for Software Design Descriptions, copyright © 1987 by the Institute of Electrical and Electronic Engineers, Inc. This information was written within the context of IEEE Std 1016-1987, and the IEEE takes no responsibility for or liability for any damages resulting from the reader's misinterpretation of said information. This information does not represent the approved and consensus standard. Information is reproduced with the permission of the IEEE.

n.6   Interfaces
Define the control and data flow to and from the component.

n.7   Resources
List the resources required, such as displays and printers.

n.8   References
Reference any documents needed to understand the component.

n.9   Processing
Describe the control and data flow within the component using pseudo-code or a PDL.

n.10 Data
Define in detail the data internal to components.

Appendix A   Source code listings
Insert listings of the code or a configuration item list showing where the code can be found.

Appendix B   Software Requirements vs Component Traceability matrix
Give a table cross-referencing components to software requirements.

C.5 SUM table of contents [7]

1   Introduction
   1.1   Intended readership
         Describe who should read the SUM.
   1.2   Applicability statement
         State which software release the SUM applies to.
   1.3   Purpose
         Describe the purpose of the document.
         Describe the purpose of the software.
   1.4   How to use this document
         Say how the document is intended to be read.
   1.5   Related documents
         Describe the place of the SUM in the project documentation.
   1.6   Conventions
         Describe any stylistic and command syntax conventions used.
   1.7   Problem reporting instructions
         Summarise the SPR system for reporting problems.

2   [Overview section]
     Describe the process to be supported by the software, and
     what the software does to support the process, and
     what the user and/or operator needs to supply to the software.

3   [Instruction section]
     From the trainee's viewpoint, for each task, provide:
       (a)   Functional description
             What the task will achieve.
       (b)   Cautions and warnings
             Do's and don'ts.
       (c)   Procedures
             Include:
               Set-up and initialisation
               Input operations
               What results to expect
       (d)   Probable errors and possible causes
             What to do when things go wrong.

---

7 Extracted from IEEE Std 1063-1987, IEEE Standard for Software User Documentation, copyright ©
1987 by the Institute of Electrical and Electronic Engineers, Inc. This information was written within the
context of IEEE Std 1063-1987, and the IEEE takes no responsibility for or liability for any damages
resulting from the reader's misinterpretation of said information. This information does not represent the
approved and consensus standard. Information is reproduced with the permission of the IEEE.

4   [Reference section]

From the expert's viewpoint, for each basic operation, provide:

    (a)   Functional description
           What the operation does.

    (b)   Cautions and warnings
           Do's and don'ts.

    (c)   Formal description
           Required parameters
           Optional parameters
           Default options
           Parameter order and syntax

    (d)   Examples
           Give worked examples of the operation.

    (e)   Possible error messages and causes
           List the possible errors and likely causes.

    (f)   Cross references to other operations
           Refer to any complementary, predecessor or successor operations.

Appendix A   Error messages and recovery procedures
                  List all the error messages.

Appendix B   Glossary
                  List all terms with specialised meanings.

Appendix C   Index (for manuals of 40 pages or more)
                  List all important terms.

C.6 STD table of contents

1 Introduction
   1.1 Purpose of the document
   1.2 Scope of the software
   1.3 Definitions, acronyms and abbreviations
   1.4 References
   1.5 Overview of the document

2 Installation Procedures
   Describe how to get the software up and running on the target machine.

3 Build Procedures
   Describe how to build the software from source code.

4 Configuration Item List
   List all the deliverable configuration items.

5 Acceptance Test Report Summary
   For each acceptance test, give the:
     user requirement identifier and summary
     test report identifier in the SVVP/AT/Test Reports
     test result summary

6 Software Problem Reports
   List the SPRs raised during the TR phase and their status at STD issue.

7 Software Change Requests
   List the SCRs raised during the TR phase and their status at STD issue.

8 Software Modification Reports
   List the SMRs completed during the TR phase.

C.7 PHD table of contents

1 Description of the project
Describe the product developed by the project, the context of the project, the constraints on the project, and the development environment.

2 Management of the project
   2.1 Contractual approach
   Describe the contractual arrangement (e.g. in-house, external contractor).
   2.2 Project organisation
   Describe the project organisation in each phase of the life cycle.
   2.3 Methods used
   List the methods and tools used.
   2.4 Planning
   Describe the original plan and what actually happened.

3 Software Production
   3.1 Estimated vs. actual amount of code produced
   Give the estimated volume of code at the end of the AD phase.
   Give the actual volume of code at the end of the TR phase.
   3.2 Documentation
   List the project documents, with the number of words and pages.
   3.3 Estimated vs. actual effort
   For each work package:
     Give the predicted man-months of effort;
     Give the actual man-months of effort.
   3.4 Computer resources
   List the computer resources predicted at the end of AD phase.
   List the computer resources used at the end of the TR phase.
   3.5 Analysis of productivity factors
   Give productivity estimates (e.g. LOC/day).

4 Quality Assurance Review
Summarise the SQA activities.

5 Financial Review
Give the total cost for each phase, and for the whole development.
For each work package:
  Give the costs predicted at the end of the UR, SR and AD phases;
  Give the actual cost.

6   Conclusions
Say whether the project was a success or failure.
Describe the lessons learned.

7   Performance of the system in OM phase
Summarise the users views on the system after final acceptance.
Record data related to quality, reliability, maintainability and safety.

C.8   SPMP table of contents [8]

Software Project Management Plan for the SR Phase

1   Introduction
    1.1   Project overview
        Summarise the project plan.
    1.2   Project deliverables
        List what will be delivered, when and where.
    1.3   Evolution of the SPMP
        Summarise the updates to this version of the SPMP.
    1.4   Reference materials
        List applicable and reference documents.
    1.5   Definitions and acronyms
        List all abbreviations and acronyms.

2   Project Organisation
    2.1   Process model
        Define the life cycle approach to the project.
    2.2   Organisational structure
        Describe project roles and reporting lines.
    2.3   Organisational boundaries and interfaces
        Describe the interfaces with customers and suppliers.
    2.4   Project responsibilities
        Describe the responsibilities of the roles described in 2.2.

3   Managerial process
    3.1   Management objectives and priorities
        Describe the management goals and priorities.
    3.2   Assumptions, dependencies and constraints
        Describe assumptions, external dependencies and constraints that influence the project plan.
    3.3   Risk management
        Describe the risks, and how they will be managed.
    3.4   Monitoring and controlling mechanisms
        Describe how the project will controlled and monitored.
    3.5   Staffing plan
        Describe the number of people required in each skill category.

---

[8] Extracted from IEEE Std 1058.1-1987, IEEE Standard for Software Project Management Plans, copyright © 1987 by the Institute of Electrical and Electronic Engineers, Inc. This information was written within the context of IEEE Std 1058.1-1987, and the IEEE takes no responsibility for or liability for any damages resulting from the reader's misinterpretation of said information. This information does not represent the approved and consensus standard. Information is reproduced with the permission of the IEEE.

4   Technical Process
    4.1   Methods, tools and techniques
        Summarise the software development methods and tools.
    4.2   Software documentation
        Define or reference the documentation plan.
    4.3   Project support functions
        Reference the plans for SCM, SVV and SQA.
        Say who will write the plans and perform the functions.

5   Work Packages, Schedule, and Budget
    5.1   Work packages
        For each work package, describe the inputs, tasks, outputs and
        verification process.
    5.2   Dependencies
        Describe the interdependencies between the work packages.
        Describe the external dependencies of the work packages.
    5.3   Resource requirements
        Describe who and what is required to do the project.
    5.4   Budget and resource allocation
        Allocate the resources to the work packages.
    5.5   Schedule
        Describe when the work packages will be done.

Software Project Management Plan for the AD Phase   ⎤   Same
Software Project Management Plan for the DD Phase   structure as
Software Project Management Plan for the TR Phase   ⎦   SPMP/SR

C.9 SCMP table of contents [9]

Software Configuration Management Plan for the SR Phase

1   Introduction
    1.1 Purpose of the plan
    1.2 Scope of the plan
    1.3 Glossary
    1.4 References

2   SCM Management
    2.1 Organisation
        Describe SCM roles, responsibilities and reporting lines.
    2.2 SCM Responsibilities
        List the people who will perform the roles described in 2.1.
    2.3 Applicable policies, directives and procedures
        Describe any external policies, directives and procedures.

3   SCM Activities
    3.1 Configuration Identification
        Describe the CI identification conventions.
        For each baseline:
            Describe when it will be created;
            Describe what it will contain;
            Describe how it will be established;
            Describe the level of authority required to change it.
    3.2 Configuration Control
        Describe the procedures for storing CIs in software libraries.
        Describe the procedures for storing media containing CIs.
        Describe the change control procedures.
    3.3 Configuration Status Accounting
        Describe the procedures for keeping an audit trail of changes.
    3.4 Interface Control
        Describe the change control process for any ICDs.
    3.5 Supplier Control
        *Describe the procedures for incorporating and controlling changes
        to externally supplied items.*

---

9 Extracted from IEEE Std 828-1990, IEEE Standard for Software Configuration Management Plans, copyright © 1990 by the Institute of Electrical and Electronic Engineers, Inc. This information was written within the context of IEEE Std 828-1990, and the IEEE takes no responsibility for or liability for any damages resulting from the reader's misinterpretation of said information. This information does not represent the approved and consensus standard. Information is reproduced with the permission of the IEEE.

4   SCM Schedules
     Summarise when SCM activities will be done.

5   SCM Resources
     Describe who and what is required to do SCM.

Software Configuration Management Plan for the AD Phase
Software Configuration Management Plan for the DD Phase
Software Configuration Management Plan for the TR Phase

Same
structure as
SCMP/SR

C.10 SVVP table of contents [10]

Software Verification and Validation Plan for the SR Phase

1 Purpose of the plan

2 Reference documents

3 Definitions

4 Verification and validation overview
  4.1 Organisation
      Describe SVV roles, responsibilities and reporting lines.
  4.2 Master schedule
      Summarise when SVV activities will be done.
  4.3 Resources summary
      Describe who and what is required to do SVV.
  4.4 Responsibilities
      List the people who will perform the roles described in 4.1.
  4.5 Tools, techniques and methods
      Describe the tools, techniques and methods used for SVV

5 Verification and validation administrative procedures
  5.1 Anomaly reporting and resolution
      Describe or reference the problem reporting procedures.
      Define the problem severity levels.
  5.2 Task iteration policy
      Describe the criteria for repeating tasks.
  5.3 Deviation policy
      Describe the procedure for approving deviations from the plan.
  5.4 Control procedures
      Describe or reference how SVV outputs will be controlled.
  5.5 Standards, practices and conventions
      Describe any external policies, directives and procedures.

---

10 Extracted from IEEE Std 1012-1986, IEEE Standard for Software Verification and Validation Plans, copyright © 1986 by the Institute of Electrical and Electronic Engineers, Inc. This information was written within the context of IEEE Std 1012-1986, and the IEEE takes no responsibility for or liability for any damages resulting from the reader's misinterpretation of said information. This information does not represent the approved and consensus standard. Information is reproduced with the permission of the IEEE.

6   Verification and validation activities
    6.1   Traceability matrix template
        Show how to trace phase inputs to outputs.
    6.2   Formal proofs
        Show how the correctness of the phase outputs will be shown.
    6.3   Reviews
        Describe the inspection, walkthrough, technical review and audit procedures.

7   Verification and validation reporting
    Describe how the results of the activities listed in 6.1 will be reported.

Software Verification and Validation Plan for the AD Phase

Software Verification and Validation Plan for the DD Phase

Same structure as SVVP/SR

Acceptance Test Specification[11]
  1   Test Plan
        1.1   Introduction
              Summarise the software items and features to be tested.
        1.2   Test items
              List the items to be tested.
        1.3   Features to be tested
              List the features to be tested.
        1.4   Features not to be tested
              List the features not to be tested.
        1.5   Approach
              Outline how the tests will be done.
        1.6   Item pass/fail criteria
              Specify the criteria for passing or failing a test.
        1.7   Suspension criteria and resumption requirements
              Specify the criteria for stopping or resuming a test.
        1.8   Test deliverables
              List the items that must be delivered before testing starts.
              List the items that must be delivered when testing ends.
        1.9   Testing tasks
              Describe the tasks needed to prepare for and carry out the tests.
      1.10   Environmental needs
              Describe the properties required of the test environment.
      1.11   Responsibilities
              Describe who will:
                authorise testing is ready to start;
                perform the tests;
                check the results;
                authorise testing is complete.
      1.12   Staffing and training needs
              Describe test staffing needs by skill level.
              Identify training requirements for the necessary skills.
      1.13   Schedule
              Summarise when test activities will be done.
      1.14   Risks and contingencies
              Identify the high-risk assumptions of this plan.
              Describe the contingency plan for each.

    1.15 Approvals
          Specify who must approve this plan.

2   Test Designs (for each test design...)
    2.n.1 Test design identifier
          Give a unique identifier for the test design.
    2.n.2 Features to be tested
          List the features to be tested.
    2.n.3 Approach refinements
          Describe how the tests will be done.
    2.n.4 Test case identification
          List the specific test cases.
    2.n.5 Feature pass/fail criteria
          Specify the criteria for passing or failing a test.

3   Test Case Specifications (for each test case...)
    3.n.1 Test case identifier
          Give a unique identifier for the test case.
    3.n.2 Test items
          List the items to be tested.
    3.n.3 Input specifications
          Describe the input for the test case.
    3.n.4 Output specifications
          Describe the output required from the test case.
    3.n.5 Environmental needs
          Describe the test environment.
    3.n.6 Special procedural requirements
          Describe any special constraints on this test.
    3.n.7 Intercase dependencies
          List the test cases that must precede this test case.

4   Test Procedures (for each test case...)
    4.n.1 Test procedure identifier
          Give a unique identifier for the test procedure.
    4.n.2 Purpose
          Describe the purpose of the procedure.
          List the test cases this procedure executes.
    4.n.3 Special requirements
          Describe any special constraints on this test.
    4.n.4 Procedure steps
          Describe how to log, setup, start, proceed, measure,
          shut down, restart, stop, wrap the test, and
          how to handle contingencies.

5   Test Reports (for each execution of a test procedure ...)

    5.n.1   Test report identifier
            Give a unique identifier for the test report.

    5.n.2   Description
            List the items being tested.

    5.n.3   Activity and event entries
            Identify the test procedure.
            Say when the test was done, who did it, and who witnessed it.
            Describe the environmental conditions.
            Describe what happened.
            Describe where the outputs of the test procedure are kept.

System Test Specification   ]   Same
Integration Test Specification   structure as
Unit Test Specification (may be in DDD)   SVVP/AT

C.11   SQAP table of contents [12]

Software Quality Assurance Plan for the SR phase

1   Purpose of the plan

2   Reference documents

3   Management
Describe how the implementation of the SPMP will be verified.

4   Documentation
Describe how the conformance of the documentation to these standards, and any project conventions, will be verified.

5   Standards, practices, conventions and metrics
Identify the standards, practices and conventions to be applied.
State how compliance will be monitored.
List the metrics to be applied and the approach to data collection.

6   Review and audits
Describe how the conduct of technical reviews, inspections, walkthroughs and audits will be monitored.

7   Test
Describe how the testing activities will be monitored.

8   Problem reporting and corrective action
Describe how adherence to problem reporting procedures will be monitored, and how the adequacy of the response of the project will be checked.

9   Tools, techniques and methods
Identify the tools, techniques and methods used.
Describe how their use will be monitored.

10   Code control
Describe how adherence to the procedures described in the SCMP for storing CIs in software libraries will be monitored.

11   Media control
Describe how adherence to the procedures described in the SCMP for storing media containing CIs will be monitored.

12   Supplier control
Describe how adherence to the supplier control procedures stated in the SCMP will be monitored.

13   Records collection, maintenance and retention
Describe how the retention of all records, such as reports and configuration status accounts, will be monitored.

---

[12] Extracted from IEEE Std 730-1989, IEEE Standard for Software Quality Assurance Plans, copyright © 1989 by the Institute of Electrical and Electronic Engineers, Inc. This information was written within the context of IEEE Std 730-1989, and the IEEE takes no responsibility for or liability for any damages resulting from the reader's misinterpretation of said information. This information does not represent the approved and consensus standard. Information is reproduced with the permission of the IEEE.

14   Training
     Describe how the level of training of all development staff
     will be checked.
15   Risk Management
     State how the risk management process described in the SPMP
     will be monitored.
16   Outline of the rest of the project
     Updated every phase.

Software Quality Assurance Plan for the AD Phase ⎤ Same
Software Quality Assurance Plan for the DD Phase ⎥ structure as
Software Quality Assurance Plan for the TR Phase ⎦ SQAP/SR

APPENDIX D
SUMMARY OF MANDATORY PRACTICES

These mandatory practices have been extracted for ease of reference, and can be used as a review checklist. They are labelled with the chapter they come from, suffixed with a sequence number. This number corresponds to the order of the requirement in the chapter.

D.1 SOFTWARE LIFE CYCLE

SLC01   The products of a software development project shall be delivered in a timely manner and be fit for their purpose.

SLC02   Software development activities shall be systematically planned and carried out.

SLC03   All software projects shall have a life cycle approach which includes the basic phases shown in Part 1, Figure 1.1:

UR phase	-	Definition of the user requirements
SR phase	-	Definition of the software requirements
AD phase	-	Definition of the architectural design
DD phase	-	Detailed design and production of the code
TR phase	-	Transfer of the software to operations
OM phase	-	Operations and maintenance

D.2 UR PHASE

UR01   The definition of the user requirements shall be the responsibility of the user.

UR02   Each user requirement shall include an identifier.

UR03   Essential user requirements shall be marked as such.

UR04   For incremental delivery, each user requirement shall include a measure of priority so that the developer can decide the production schedule.

UR05   The source of each user requirement shall be stated.

UR06   Each user requirement shall be verifiable.

UR07   The user shall describe the consequences of losses of availability, or breaches of security, so that developers can fully appreciate the criticality of each function.

UR08   The outputs of the UR phase shall be formally reviewed during the User Requirements Review.

UR09   Non-applicable user requirements shall be clearly flagged in the URD.

UR10   An output of the UR phase shall be the User Requirements Document (URD).

UR11   The URD shall always be produced before a software project is started.

UR12   The URD shall provide a general description of what the user expects the software to do.

UR13   All known user requirements shall be included in the URD.

UR14   The URD shall describe the operations the user wants to perform with the software system.

UR15   The URD shall define all the constraints that the user wishes to impose upon any solution.

UR16   The URD shall describe the external interfaces to the software system or reference them in ICDs that exist or are to be written.

D.3   SR PHASE

SR01   SR phase activities shall be carried out according to the plans defined in the UR phase.

SR02   The developer shall construct an implementation-independent model of what is needed by the user.

SR03   A recognised method for software requirements analysis shall be adopted and applied consistently in the SR phase.

SR04   Each software requirement shall include an identifier.

SR05   Essential software requirements shall be marked as such.

SR06   For incremental delivery, each software requirement shall include a measure of priority so that the developer can decide the production schedule.

SR07   References that trace software requirements back to the URD shall accompany each software requirement.

SR08   Each software requirement shall be verifiable.

SR09   The outputs of the SR phase shall be formally reviewed during the Software Requirements Review.

SR10   An output of the SR phase shall be the Software Requirements Document (SRD).

SR11   The SRD shall be complete.

SR12   The SRD shall cover all the requirements stated in the URD.

SR13   A table showing how user requirements correspond to software requirements shall be placed in the SRD.

SR14   The SRD shall be consistent.

SR15   The SRD shall not include implementation details or terminology, unless it has to be present as a constraint.

SR16   Descriptions of functions ... shall say what the software is to do, and must avoid saying how it is to be done.

SR17   The SRD shall avoid specifying the hardware or equipment, unless it is a constraint placed by the user.

SR18   The SRD shall be compiled according to the table of contents provided in Appendix C.

D.4   AD PHASE

AD01   AD phase activities shall be carried out according to the plans defined in the SR phase.

AD02   A recognised method for software design shall be adopted and applied consistently in the AD phase.

AD03   The developer shall construct a 'physical model', which describes the design of the software using implementation terminology.

AD04   The method used to decompose the software into its component parts shall permit a top-down approach.

AD05   Only the selected design approach shall be reflected in the ADD.

For each component the following information shall be detailed in the ADD:

AD06   •   data input;

AD07   •   functions to be performed;

AD08   •   data output.

AD09   Data structures that interface components shall be defined in the ADD.

Data structure definitions shall include the:

AD10   •   description of each element (e.g. name, type, dimension);

AD11   •   relationships between the elements (i.e. the structure);

AD12   •   range of possible values of each element;

AD13   •   initial values of each element.

AD14   The control flow between the components shall be defined in the ADD.

AD15   The computer resources (e.g. CPU speed, memory, storage, system software) needed in the development environment and the operational environment shall be estimated in the AD phase and defined in the ADD.

AD16   The outputs of the AD phase shall be formally reviewed during the Architectural Design Review.

AD17   The ADD shall define the major components of the software and the interfaces between them.

AD18   The ADD shall define or reference all external interfaces.

AD19   The ADD shall be an output from the AD phase.

AD20   The ADD shall be complete, covering all the software requirements described in the SRD.

AD21   A table cross-referencing software requirements to parts of the architectural design shall be placed in the ADD.

AD22   The ADD shall be consistent.

AD23 The ADD shall be sufficiently detailed to allow the project leader to draw up a detailed implementation plan and to control the overall project during the remaining development phases.

AD24 The ADD shall be compiled according to the table of contents provided in Appendix C.

D.5 DD PHASE

DD01 DD phase activities shall be carried out according to the plans defined in the AD phase.

The detailed design and production of software shall be based on the following three principles:

DD02 • top-down decomposition;

DD03 • structured programming;

DD04 • concurrent production and documentation.

DD05 The integration process shall be controlled by the software configuration management procedures defined in the SCMP.

DD06 Before a module can be accepted, every statement in a module shall be executed successfully at least once.

DD07 Integration testing shall check that all the data exchanged across an interface agrees with the data structure specifications in the ADD.

DD08 Integration testing shall confirm that the control flows defined in the ADD have been implemented.

DD09 System testing shall verify compliance with system objectives, as stated in the SRD.

DD10 When the design of a major component is finished, a critical design review shall be convened to certify its readiness for implementation.

DD11 After production, the DD Review (DD/R) shall consider the results of the verification activities and decide whether to transfer the software.

DD12 All deliverable code shall be identified in a configuration item list.

DD13 The DDD shall be an output of the DD phase.

DD14 Part 2 of the DDD shall have the same structure and identification scheme as the code itself, with a 1:1 correspondence between sections of the documentation and the software components.

DD15 The DDD shall be complete, accounting for all the software requirements in the SRD.

DD16 A table cross-referencing software requirements to the detailed design components shall be placed in the DDD.

DD17 A Software User Manual (SUM) shall be an output of the DD phase.

D.6 TR PHASE

TR01 Representatives of users and operations personnel shall participate in acceptance tests.

TR02 The Software Review Board (SRB) shall review the software's performance in the acceptance tests and recommend, to the initiator, whether the software can be provisionally accepted or not.

TR03 TR phase activities shall be carried out according to the plans defined in the DD phase.

TR04 The capability of building the system from the components that are directly modifiable by the maintenance team shall be established.

TR05 Acceptance tests necessary for provisional acceptance shall be indicated in the SVVP.

TR06 The statement of provisional acceptance shall be produced by the initiator, on behalf of the users, and sent to the developer.

TR07 The provisionally accepted software system shall consist of the outputs of all previous phases and modifications found necessary in the TR phase.

TR08 An output of the TR phase shall be the STD.

TR09 The STD shall be handed over from the developer to the maintenance organisation at provisional acceptance.

TR10 The STD shall contain the summary of the acceptance test reports, and all documentation about software changes performed during the TR phase.

D.7 OM PHASE

OM01 Until final acceptance, OM phase activities that involve the developer shall be carried out according to the plans defined in the SPMP/TR.

OM02 All the acceptance tests shall have been successfully completed before the software is finally accepted.

OM03 Even when no contractor is involved, there shall be a final acceptance milestone to arrange the formal hand-over from software development to maintenance.

OM04 A maintenance organisation shall be designated for every software product in operational use.

OM05 Procedures for software modification shall be defined.

OM06 Consistency between code and documentation shall be maintained.

OM07 Resources shall be assigned to a product's maintenance until it is retired.

OM08 The SRB ... shall authorise all modifications to the software.

OM09 The statement of final acceptance shall be produced by the initiator, on behalf of the users, and sent to the developer.

OM10 The PHD shall be delivered to the initiator after final acceptance.

D.8 SOFTWARE PROJECT MANAGEMENT

SPM01 All software project management activities shall be documented in the Software Project Management Plan (SPMP).

SPM02 By the end of the UR review, the SR phase section of the SPMP shall be produced (SPMP/SR).

SPM03 The SPMP/SR shall outline a plan for the whole project.

SPM04   A precise estimate of the effort involved in the SR phase shall be included in the SPMP/SR.

SPM05   During the SR phase, the AD phase section of the SPMP shall be produced (SPMP/AD).

SPM06   An estimate of the total project cost shall be included in the SPMP/AD.

SPM07   A precise estimate of the effort involved in the AD phase shall be included in the SPMP/AD.

SPM08   During the AD phase, the DD phase section of the SPMP shall be produced (SPMP/DD).

SPM09   An estimate of the total project cost shall be included in the SPMP/DD.

SPM10   The SPMP/DD shall contain a WBS that is directly related to the decomposition of the software into components.

SPM11   The SPMP/DD shall contain a planning network showing relationships of coding, integration and testing activities.

SPM12   No software production work packages in the SPMP/DD shall last longer than 1 man-month.

SPM13   During the DD phase, the TR phase section of the SPMP shall be produced (SPMP/TR).

D.9   SOFTWARE CONFIGURATION MANAGEMENT

SCM01   All software items, for example documentation, source code, object or relocatable code, executable code, files, tools, test software and data, shall be subjected to configuration management procedures.

SCM02   The configuration management procedures shall establish methods for identifying, storing and changing software items through development, integration and transfer.

SCM03   A common set of configuration management procedures shall be used.
Every configuration item shall have an identifier that distinguishes it from other items with different:

SCM04   •   requirements, especially functionality and interfaces;

SCM05   •   implementation.

SCM06   Each component defined in the design process shall be designated as a CI and include an identifier.

SCM07   The identifier shall include a number or a name related to the purpose of the CI.

SCM08   The identifier shall include an indication of the type of processing the CI is intended for (e.g. filetype information).

SCM09   The identifier of a CI shall include a version number.

SCM10   The identifier of documents shall include an issue number and a revision number.

SCM11   The configuration identification method shall be capable of accommodating new CIs, without requiring the modification of the identifiers of any existing CIs.

SCM12	In the TR phase, a list of configuration items in the first release shall be included in the STD.
SCM13	In the OM phase, a list of changed configuration items shall be included in each Software Release Note (SRN).
SCM14	An SRN shall accompany each release made in the OM phase.

As part of the configuration identification method, a software module shall have a standard header that includes:

SCM15	• configuration item identifier (name, type, version);
SCM16	• original author;
SCM17	• creation date;
SCM18	• change history (version/date/author/description).

All documentation and storage media shall be clearly labelled in a standard format, with at least the following data:

SCM19	• project name;
SCM20	• configuration item identifier (name, type, version);
SCM21	• date;
SCM22	• content description.

To ensure security and control of the software, at a minimum, the following software libraries shall be implemented for storing all the deliverable components (e.g. documentation, source and executable code, test files, command procedures):

SCM23	• Development (or Dynamic) library;
SCM24	• Master (or Controlled) library;
SCM25	• Static (or Archive) library.
SCM26	Static libraries shall not be modified.
SCM27	Up-to-date security copies of master and static libraries shall always be available.
SCM28	Procedures for the regular backup of development libraries shall be established.
SCM29	The change procedure described (in Part 2, Section 3.2.3.2.1) shall be observed when changes are needed to a delivered document.
SCM30	Software problems and change proposals shall be handled by the procedure described (in Part 2, Section 3.2.3.2).
SCM31	The status of all configuration items shall be recorded.

To perform software status accounting, each software project shall record:

SCM32	• the date and version/issue of each baseline;
SCM33	• the date and status of each RID and DCR;
SCM34	• the date and status of each SPR, SCR and SMR;
SCM35	• a summary description of each Configuration Item.
SCM36	As a minimum, the SRN shall record the faults that have been repaired and the new requirements that have been incorporated.
SCM37	For each release, documentation and code shall be consistent.
SCM38	Old releases shall be retained, for reference.

SCM39 Modified software shall be retested before release.

SCM40 All software configuration management activities shall be documented in the Software Configuration Management Plan (SCMP).

SCM41 Configuration management procedures shall be in place before the production of software (code and documentation) starts.

SCM42 By the end of the UR review, the SR phase section of the SCMP shall be produced (SCMP/SR).

SCM43 The SCMP/SR shall cover the configuration management procedures for documentation, and any CASE tool outputs or prototype code, to be produced in the SR phase.

SCM44 During the SR phase, the AD phase section of the SCMP shall be produced (SCMP/AD).

SCM45 The SCMP/AD shall cover the configuration management procedures for documentation, and CASE tool outputs or prototype code, to be produced in the AD phase.

SCM46 During the AD phase, the DD phase section of the SCMP shall be produced (SCMP/DD).

SCM47 The SCMP/DD shall cover the configuration management procedures for documentation, deliverable code, and any CASE tool outputs or prototype code, to be produced in the DD phase.

SCM48 During the DD phase, the TR phase section of the SCMP shall be produced (SCMP/TR).

SCM49 The SCMP/TR shall cover the procedures for the configuration management of the deliverables in the operational environment.

D.10 SOFTWARE VERIFICATION AND VALIDATION

SVV01 Forwards traceability requires that each input to a phase shall be traceable to an output of that phase.

SVV02 Backwards traceability requires that each output of a phase shall be traceable to an input to that phase.

SVV03 Functional and physical audits shall be performed before the release of the software.

SVV04 All software verification and validation activities shall be documented in the Software Verification and Validation Plan (SVVP).

The SVVP shall ensure that the verification activities:

SVV05 • are appropriate for the degree of criticality of the software;

SVV06 • meet the verification and acceptance testing requirements (stated in the SRD);

SVV07 • verify that the product will meet the quality, reliability, maintainability and safety requirements (stated in the SRD);

SVV08 •• are sufficient to assure the quality of the product.

SVV09 By the end of the UR review, the SR phase section of the SVVP shall be produced (SVVP/SR).

SVV10	The SVVP/SR shall define how to trace user requirements to software requirements, so that each software requirement can be justified.
SVV11	The developer shall construct an acceptance test plan in the UR phase and document it in the SVVP.
SVV12	During the SR phase, the AD phase section of the SVVP shall be produced (SVVP/AD).
SVV13	The SVVP/AD shall define how to trace software requirements to components, so that each software component can be justified.
SVV14	The developer shall construct a system test plan in the SR phase and document it in the SVVP.
SVV15	During the AD phase, the DD phase section of the SVVP shall be produced (SVVP/DD).
SVV16	The SVVP/AD shall describe how the DDD and code are to be evaluated by defining the review and traceability procedures.
SVV17	The developer shall construct an integration test plan in the AD phase and document it in the SVVP.
SVV18	The developer shall construct a unit test plan in the DD phase and document it in the SVVP.
SVV19	The unit, integration, system and acceptance test designs shall be described in the SVVP.
SVV20	The unit integration, system and acceptance test cases shall be described in the SVVP.
SVV21	The unit, integration, system and acceptance test procedures shall be described in the SVVP.
SVV22	The unit, integration, system and acceptance test reports shall be described in the SVVP.

D.11 SOFTWARE QUALITY ASSURANCE

SQA01	An SQAP shall be produced by each contractor developing software.
SQA02	All software quality assurance activities shall be documented in the Software Quality Assurance Plan (SQAP).
SQA03	By the end of the UR review, the SR phase section of the SQAP shall be produced (SQAP/SR).
SQA04	The SQAP/SR shall describe, in detail, the quality assurance activities to be carried out in the SR phase.
SQA05	The SQAP/SR shall outline the quality assurance plan for the rest of the project.
SQA06	During the SR phase, the AD phase section of the SQAP shall be produced (SQAP/AD).
SQA07	The SQAP/AD shall cover in detail all the quality assurance activities to be carried out in the AD phase.
SQA08	During the AD phase, the DD phase section of the SQAP shall be produced (SQAP/DD).

SQA09   The SQAP/DD shall cover in detail all the quality assurance activities to be carried out in the DD phase.

SQA10   During the DD phase, the TR phase section of the SQAP shall be produced (SQAP/TR).

SQA11   The SQAP/TR shall cover in detail all the quality assurance activities to be carried out from the start the TR phase until final acceptance in the OM phase.

APPENDIX E
FORM TEMPLATES

Template forms are provided for:
    DCR -   Document Change Record
    DSS -   Document Status Sheet
    RID -   Review Item Discrepancy
    SCR -   Software Change Request
    SMR -   Software Modification Report
    SPR -   Software Problem Report
    SRN -   Software Release Note

DOCUMENT CHANGE RECORD	DCR NO	
	DATE	
	ORIGINATOR	
	APPROVED BY	

1. DOCUMENT TITLE:

2. DOCUMENT REFERENCE NUMBER:

3. DOCUMENT ISSUE/REVISION NUMBER:

4. PAGE	5. PARAGRAPH	6. REASON FOR CHANGE

DOCUMENT STATUS SHEET			
1. DOCUMENT TITLE:			
2. DOCUMENT REFERENCE NUMBER:			
3. ISSUE	4. REVISION	5. DATE	6. REASON FOR CHANGE

REVIEW ITEM DISCREPANCY	RID NO	
	DATE	
	ORIGINATOR	

1. DOCUMENT TITLE:

2. DOCUMENT REFERENCE NUMBER:

3. DOCUMENT ISSUE/REVISION NUMBER:

4. PROBLEM LOCATION:

5. PROBLEM DESCRIPTION:

6. RECOMMENDED SOLUTION:

7. AUTHOR'S RESPONSE:

8. REVIEW DECISION: CLOSE/UPDATE/ACTION/REJECT (underline choice)

SOFTWARE CHANGE REQUEST	SCR NO	
	DATE	
	ORIGINATOR	
	RELATED SPRs	

1. SOFTWARE ITEM TITLE:

2. SOFTWARE ITEM VERSION/RELEASE NUMBER:

3. PRIORITY: CRITICAL/URGENT/ROUTINE (underline choice)

4. CHANGES REQUIRED:

5. RESPONSIBLE STAFF:

6. ESTIMATED START DATE, END DATE AND MANPOWER EFFORT:

7. ATTACHMENTS:

SOFTWARE MODIFICATION REPORT	SMR NO	
	DATE	
	ORIGINATOR	
	RELATED SCRs	

1. SOFTWARE ITEM TITLE:

2. SOFTWARE ITEM VERSION/RELEASE NUMBER:

3. CHANGES IMPLEMENTED:

4. ACTUAL START DATE, END DATE AND MANPOWER EFFORT:

5. ATTACHMENTS	Source Code		(tick as appropriate)
	Test Procedures		
	Test Data		
	Test Results		
	Documentation Updates		

SOFTWARE PROBLEM REPORT	SPR NO	
	DATE	
	ORIGINATOR	

1. SOFTWARE ITEM TITLE:

2. SOFTWARE ITEM VERSION/RELEASE NUMBER:

3. PRIORITY: CRITICAL/URGENT/ROUTINE (underline choice)

4. PROBLEM DESCRIPTION:

5. DESCRIPTION OF ENVIRONMENT:

6. RECOMMENDED SOLUTION:

7. REVIEW DECISION: CLOSE/UPDATE/ACTION/REJECT (underline choice)

8. ATTACHMENTS:

SOFTWARE RELEASE NOTE	SRN NO	
	DATE	
	ORIGINATOR	
	APPROVED BY	

1. SOFTWARE ITEM TITLE:

2. SOFTWARE ITEM VERSION/RELEASE NUMBER:

3. CHANGES IN THIS RELEASE:

4. CONFIGURATION ITEMS INCLUDED IN THIS RELEASE:

5. INSTALLATION INSTRUCTIONS:

INDEX